Green Cleaning
FOR
DUMMIES
ISSA SPECIAL EDITION

by Stephen Ashkin and David Holly

BICENTENNIAL
1807
WILEY
2007
BICENTENNIAL

Wiley Publishing, Inc.

Green Cleaning For Dummies®, ISSA Special Edition

Published by
Wiley Publishing, Inc.
111 River St.
Hoboken, NJ 07030-5774
www.wiley.com

WILEY

About the Authors

Steve Ashkin has been a leader in the green cleaning movement since long before it was even recognized as a movement. His efforts in pioneering many of the concepts that are now taken for granted has led to his being thought of as the "Father of Green Cleaning." Steve is President of The Ashkin Group, LLC., and has been in the cleaning industry for over 25 years where he has held senior management positions in leading commercial and consumer product companies. Steve has been a leader in the effort to green the cleaning industry since 1990 and is a prolific writer, speaker, and advocate for greener, safer, healthier and more sustainable cleaning.

David Holly has been involved in the cleaning industry for almost 30 years, working in virtually every facet of the business. David was the Vice President of a regional cleaning contractor, Director of Sales & Marketing for S.C. Johnson Professional, and Director of Marketing for Multi-Clean. He is now President of Don't Panic Productions, Inc., a new media development company that produces marketing and training materials for companies in the cleaning industry. David is a frequent speaker at conferences in the United States as well as internationally and devotes the majority of his time to green cleaning issues.

Authors' Acknowledgments

We would like to acknowledge the contributions made by so many to help us along our journey as we have come to understand the responsibility we have to make the world a better place. To begin, we want to thank God for the many blessings in our lives along with our parents, Abraham and Arleen Ashkin and Duane and Emma Holly, our wives Elizabeth Ashkin and Karen Holly and our amazing children, Adrianne and Alexander Ashkin and Emma and Rachel Holly to whom we dedicate this book; for without children there is no future. We want to thank our advisors whose wise counsel we very much value and appreciate including Michael Arny, Peter Ashkin, Laura Brannen, Rochelle Davis, Christine Ervin, Lloyd Kolbe, Richard Liroff, Barbara Sattler, and Sheila Sheridan. And those who have helped and inspired us along the way and who have been major contributors to the success of the green cleaning movement including Darryl Alexander, Dana Arnold, Bob Axelrad, Elizabeth Blackburn, Denise Bowles, Hillary Brown, Robert Bullard, Ross Cameron, Scot Case, Joy Carlson, Lee Chen, James Darr, Heather Davies, Marcia Deegler, Dick Dow, Richard Ellis, Richard Fedrizzi, Eric Friedman, Lois Gibbs, Eun-Sook Goidel, David Gottfried, Richard Gross, Michael Italiano, Bob Kobet, Roger McFadden, Paul von Paumgartten, Mark Petruzzi, John Russell, Julie Shannon, Ron Segura, John Walley, Robert Watson, and Arthur Weissman. Finally, we would like to thank ISSA for making this book happen. ISSA has demonstrated real leadership and we especially want to recognize John Garfinkel, William Balek, Dianna Bisswurm, Anthony Trombetta, Daniel Wagner, and Martha Reynoso, along with the ISSA Board of Directors and all of its members. Together we really are making a difference.

Publisher's Acknowledgments

We're proud of this book; please send us your comments through our Dummies online registration form located at www.dummies.com/register/.

Some of the people who helped bring this book to market include the following:

Acquisitions, Editorial, and Media Development

Project Editor: Jennifer Bingham

Development Editor: Traci Cumbay

Business Development Representative: Jacqueline Smith

Editorial Manager: Rev Mengle

Cartoons: Rich Tennant (www.the5thwave.com)

Composition Services

Project Coordinator: Kristie Rees

Layout and Graphics: LeAndra Hosier, Erin Zeltner

Anniversary Logo Design: Richard Pacifico

Proofreaders: Melissa Buddendeck, Brian H. Walls

Indexer: Sherry Massey

Publishing and Editorial for Consumer Dummies

   Diane Graves Steele, Vice President and Publisher, Consumer Dummies

   Joyce Pepple, Acquisitions Director, Consumer Dummies

   Kristin A. Cocks, Product Development Director, Consumer Dummies

   Michael Spring, Vice President and Publisher, Travel

   Kelly Regan, Editorial Director, Travel

Publishing for Technology Dummies

   Andy Cummings, Vice President and Publisher, Dummies Technology/General User

Composition Services

   Gerry Fahey, Vice President of Production Services

   Debbie Stailey, Director of Composition Services

Table of Contents

Introduction

• •

Close your eyes, think of the word *environment,* and see what appears in your mind's eye.

Do the same thing with *office building.*

And, finally, close your eyes and think for a moment about the word *clean.*

We often start our large group presentations with this exercise. Then we ask the audience what they see in their mind's eye when they hear those words. Typical answers include:

✔ Mountains, lakes, ocean, trees, fields, flowers, and so on for *environment*

✔ Skyscraper, desks, elevators, carpet, offices, chairs, and such for *office building*

✔ Mops, buckets, brooms, wet floor signs, dirt, and so on for *clean*

Were your answers similar? The interesting thing about all of these answers — and we hear them time after time — is that no one ever mentions *people.* People have been conditioned to see the environment, offices (or other buildings), and cleaning as something separate from themselves.

The reality is that everything you do has an impact on the people around you and on the environment as a whole. People spend more than 90 percent of their time indoors. The quality of that indoor environment has a dramatic impact on health and well-being. The care given to that indoor environment has a dramatic impact on *its* well-being. And how you find, manufacture, and dispose of your cleaning products has a dramatic impact on the environment as a whole, which impacts not only your choices in the future, but also the quality of many lives today.

About This Book

We wrote this book to help you understand the impacts of cleaning on health, well-being, and the environment. In it, we explore the basic concepts of green cleaning, its vital importance, and the ways you can implement green cleaning in your facility or for your organization.

We respect your time and deliver just the information you need, as quickly and succinctly as possible. We hope to stir your interest in the subject and challenge you to join us in carrying this important effort to even higher levels.

Advancing the case for green cleaning is our business, but it's also much more than that: It's our mission. We hope you enjoy the book, discover some new things, and spark your interest to learn even more. We also hope you'll let us know how you're doing as you begin and continue your own green journey. You can contact us at `www.GreenCleaningForDummies.com`.

About the ISSA

ISSA, the sponsor of *Green Cleaning For Dummies,* is the leading trade association for the institutional and industrial cleaning industry. ISSA's worldwide membership includes more than 4,800 companies including manufacturers and distributors of cleaning products, in addition to building service contractors and in-house cleaning service providers.

Our association members provide cleaning products and services that are ultimately consumed by schools, hospitals, day care centers, food service establishments, hotels, office buildings, retail facilities, and other institutional and industrial establishments. In this regard, our membership plays a key role in maintaining the health and sanitation of the built environment.

ISSA and its membership recognizes that environmental preferability is the new mantra of the business community as smart companies across all industry sectors use environmental based strategies to innovate, create value, and build competitive advantage, while minimizing their environmental footprint.

Nowhere is this more apparent than in the cleaning industry where green cleaning has taken firm hold in the marketplace and continues to flourish. Employee and occupant safety and health have also taken center stage as the business community embraces practices, programs, and other activities intended to promote the well-being of those who work or otherwise spend time in the built environment.

Recognizing the importance of these trends, ISSA has assumed a leadership role in promoting the widespread adoption of environmentally preferable cleaning products and services, as well as practices that promote the safety and health of workers and other building occupants. The following is a brief list of some of ISSA's current activities in this regard:

- **ISSA/DfE Alliance:** ISSA and the U.S. Environmental Protection Agency Design for the Environment (DfE) have entered into a formal alliance that facilitates and otherwise encourages the development of environmentally preferable cleaning products.

- **CleanGredients:** ISSA is a sponsor and sits on the steering committee of CleanGredients, an online database of cleaning product ingredients with a preferred environmental and safety and health profile, intended to foster the proliferation of green products.

- **Safer Detergents Stewardship Initiative:** ISSA is working in support of the Safer Detergents Stewardship Initiative (SDSI), a voluntary program that fosters the development of cleaning products with surfactant ingredients that have a preferred environmental profile.

- **ISSA Safety and Health Portal:** ISSA has created a one-of-a-kind Web network (www.issa.gov/osha) dedicated exclusively to the protection of the health and safety of workers in the cleaning industry, the latest step in the association's ongoing alliance with the U.S. Occupational Safety and Health Administration (OSHA).

Who Should Read This Book?

Like any authors, we're convinced that our book should be read by the widest audience possible. In fact, we could argue that because everyone is impacted by their indoor environment, the information in here should be required reading.

Realistically, the most common groups of people who will benefit from reading this book are:

- **Building owners and managers:** You find the information you need to respond to your tenants' requests for a green building. You also discover why you should consider moving in a greener direction *before* the requests start.

✔ **Building operations managers:** You're usually tasked with making things happen in the building. In this book, you find the step-by-step procedures to implementing a green cleaning program, how to choose the right products and equipment, as well as how to involve all the stakeholders in your facility to ensure success.

✔ **Contract cleaning company owners and managers:** Have your clients been asking about "this green cleaning stuff" yet? If not, they will be very soon. In this book, you find not only the answers to their questions, but what you need to know to keep yourself at the front edge of the movement. Not only can you solve your current clients' needs, but you'll be prepared to seek out new clients as well.

✔ **Cleaning chemical, janitorial paper, tool, and equipment manufacturers and distributors:** You've already been responding to marketplace pressures to produce and sell green chemicals, paper, tools, and equipment. When you understand the material in this book, you're in a better position to lead your customers on their green journeys. Doing so improves your relationship with current customers and helps you differentiate yourself from the competition.

✔ **Advocates, policymakers, and others trying to implement a green cleaning program:** Because this book contains all the information you need to fully implement a green cleaning program, it's a valuable resource to help you achieve your goals.

You don't have to be in building management, operations, or even a part of the cleaning industry to find value in this book. As a concerned citizen or building occupant, you can find out how cleaning impacts your health and well-being. You come to appreciate the choices that have to be made in designing an effective green cleaning program, your role in ensuring the success of the program, and how you can influence the direction taken in your building. You also begin to understand the impact on the environment as a whole, how critical it is that we start making informed choices now, and what you can do to be a leader in the effort.

It's natural to wonder what impact you as a single individual or part of a stewardship team can have in the grand scheme of things. We can't express our thoughts on this any better than in the words of Margaret Mead when she said, "Never doubt that a small group of thoughtful committed citizens can change the world. In fact, it's the only thing that ever has."

How This Book Is Organized

You can read this book from cover to cover, but *Green Cleaning For Dummies* is designed so that you can start in whatever part interests you or applies most directly to your current needs. We divided the information into four sections to help you quickly find what you're looking for. The following sections show you what you can expect.

Part 1: Beginning the Green Cleaning Journey

New to green cleaning? This may be the best place to start. In this part, we give you an overview of the concept, its principles, and the process by which green cleaning programs are effectively implemented. We do a little comparing and contrasting of green cleaning and traditional methods, and we show you the kinds of programs that others have implemented.

Part 11: Going Green

In this section, we go into more detail discussing the practical aspects of creating and implementing a green cleaning program, giving you the basics about forming the team that helps you implement change and guiding you through an assessment of your building's current state. We show you how to make your procedures greener, train your team, keep the program alive, and communicate important issues to everyone who uses the building.

Part 111: The Green Cleaning Toolbox

In this section, we drill down to the actual materials you need for your green cleaning program. Cleaning chemicals, equipment, janitorial paper products, entry matting, and other products routinely used to keep buildings clean all provide opportunities for improving health and the environment in a building.

Part 1V: The Part of Tens

If the rest of *Green Cleaning For Dummies* is a buffet, this part is a snack. Here we give you short chapters rife with tips and useful information.

Icons Used in This Book

Throughout this book we call your attention to different kinds of information with icons in the margins. Here's what they all mean:

Information marked by this icon saves you time, money, or energy.

You need to remember certain principles and ideas related to green cleaning, and we highlight those with this icon.

Sometimes we tell you a little more than you need, delving deeply into a topic we hope you find interesting but that you don't absolutely need to know about. Feel free to skip paragraphs marked by this icon.

Be careful! When we tell you about potential pitfalls along the way to a green cleaning program, we point them out with this icon.

Where to Go from Here

The field of green cleaning is dynamic and constantly evolving. No book, no matter how comprehensive, can capture the complete picture or remain current over time. We have chosen to present our discussion by focusing first on enduring principles and then looking at specifics, and finally providing suggested resources for your continued education.

We try as much as possible to provide suggestions for additional information throughout the body of this book, and we also provide a list of additional resources in the appendixes, where you find Web sites, online newsletters, books, and other publications that explore various topics in greater depth and continually provide the latest information. We also selected several organizations that we believe are deserving of our support and membership.

Finally, you can visit our companion Web site (www.GreenCleaning ForDummies.com) to communicate with the authors and find links to additional resources and discussion groups.

Part I

Beginning the Green Cleaning Journey

The 5th Wave   By Rich Tennant

"Dick has been really popular since he implemented that green cleaning program, and let's face it, that big white hat doesn't hurt either."

In this part . . .

*I*n this part, we explore the basic concepts of green cleaning and why it is so vitally important. We also give you an overview of how you can go green when you're responsible for cleaning offices, schools, and health care facilities. And finally, we show you how to let everyone in your organization know about your new green cleaning ideas and how to get them to agree to go green.

Chapter 1

Getting the Scoop on Green Cleaning

*W*hy clean?

Answers to this question reach across a surprisingly broad spectrum and in many cases miss the point. Ask the man on the street, and chances are he'd say something about keeping things neat and tidy, or getting rid of the dirt, or making a building more attractive. Ask a property manager, and she's likely to tell you that it keeps tenant complaints down. The store manager says cleaning makes shoppers more comfortable and likely to buy more products. The school administrator tells you that trash has to be emptied, paper towels replaced, and blackboards wiped for the next day. The contract cleaner might say it's in the specifications, and the janitor says it's his job.

Few if any of these people would mention protecting health, improving building occupant performance, increasing return on investment, or protecting the environment as reasons to clean.

The focus has been on appearance over the past several decades, and that's had some serious negative impacts on the cleaning industry. Because appearance is a subjective measure, what's *clean enough* can vary from day to day depending on the judge's mood, priorities, level of interest, and budget. In tough economic times, cleaning is one of the first targets for budget cuts. Instead of pulling trash daily, you cut back to two or three times per week. A little dust here and there becomes tolerable. A few carpet spots aren't a significant problem. Disinfecting public phones and computer keyboards when they don't look dirty seems unnecessary, and so on.

Over time, cleaning standards in a facility deteriorate to a point where the building materials begin to wear prematurely. Carpets that should last 10 to 15 years look worn out in less than 5 years. Tile floors that should last 25 years are stained and worn in only 10 because they haven't been protected with proper finishes and maintenance.

Cleaning has become a commodity. Lack of standards means that no matter who performs the service, the results are likely viewed as equally bad. Contractors, distributors of cleaning supplies, and other industry representatives are tolerated as necessary evils. Cleaning chemicals are assumed to be the same and compared by measuring price per gallon. Cleaning services are evaluated on the lowest cost per square foot cleaned, again all perceived as being the same.

Ironically, the focus on cleaning for appearance has in the long run had the opposite result. If you could compare before-and-after photos of some of the buildings being cleaned this way five years ago and today, the results would be eye opening.

The property owner of such a building faces a dilemma: Does he remodel and renovate (5 to 15 years *before* he planned) in order to retain and attract tenants? Does he reduce rental rates, spend money on promotions, and target a less-profitable tenant base? In either case the economic loss is significant. The cost likely dwarfs any savings realized in the previous years of cutting the cleaning budget.

As you see in the next few chapters of this book, the economic impacts of how we clean aren't limited to building materials, marketing costs, and return on investment. Cleaning has a tremendous impact on employee performance, and it has social and environmental impacts and benefits, as well.

This book was written for those of you who recognize that a change in focus is needed. The reason to clean has to be more important than appearance or meeting a budget goal. You've likely heard about green cleaning (it's hard to miss these days) and may be wondering whether it's a fad. Maybe your boss, employer, major tenant, or board of directors has directed you to implement a green cleaning program. Whatever the reason you've come to this book, *welcome!*

Before you start the journey, please take a moment to honestly answer the question, "Why clean?" for your organization. It might be interesting to compare what you've written today to your thoughts at various stages on your green cleaning journey.

Introducing Green Cleaning's Concepts

You may have some ideas about what green cleaning is and what it can do for your business and the people you work with. If you're like most people, these ideas don't necessarily align with the reality of green cleaning. In this section, we give you the straight skinny on green cleaning.

The meaning of green

Unfortunately there's no legal or regulatory definition of green or green cleaning, but the marketplace over the years has defined these terms. The most broadly accepted definition of green is laid out in Presidential Executive Order 13101. This is the definition for an "environmentally preferable" (we use this term interchangeably with green) product or service and has been widely adopted by the cleaning industry and building owners. It defines green as "products or services that have a lesser or reduced effect on health and the environment when compared with competing products or services that serve the same purpose."

Within this definition are two key points:

- ✔ The definition is *comparative* — that is, it compares products and services to existing or traditional products and services used for the same purpose. In other words, it doesn't set an absolute or final end point of what is green, nor does it suggest that current products or services are *bad* or placing product users and the environment at serious risk. Instead it encourages continual development and improvement.

- ✔ The goal of green, according to this definition, is to reduce health *and* environmental impacts. This means that green isn't simply an environmental issue but relates to human health as well. It also means that simply changing a product to be safer to use without considering the environmental impact (or vice versa) is *not* a green decision. You must consider both factors at the same time.

What makes cleaning green

We distilled all the hype and fluff to come up with the simplest definition possible: *Green cleaning* is cleaning to protect health without harming the environment. This definition captures the essence of green in addressing both health and environmental issues.

We don't suggest that current products, processes, or procedures are bad. We *do* maintain that newer technologies and processes make it possible to clean effectively, efficiently, and with less impact on health and the environment. And to be clear, green cleaning is more than switching a few products; it's about *effective* cleaning to create healthier buildings and at the same time reduce environmental impacts.

Understanding stewardship

Caring for a building, the people who use it, and the environment is an act of *stewardship* — a core tenet of green cleaning.

ASTM International (formally called the American Society for Testing and Materials; the oldest and largest standard-setting organization in the United States) compiles the Standard Guide for Stewardship for the Cleaning of Commercial and Institutional Buildings (ASTM E1971), which defines stewardship as "the responsibility for managing, conducting or supervising the quality, state or condition of a commercial or institutional building." Central to the concept of stewardship are:

- ✔ **Shared responsibility:** Reducing health and environmental impacts is a duty shared by the product manufacturers, distributors, cleaning personnel, building owners and managers, occupants, and even visitors — everyone who has an impact in or on the building. This is an incredibly important concept; for the first time in our industry, people recognize that the cleanliness, health, and safety of a building are *not* the sole responsibility of the cleaning staff.

- ✔ **Occupant responsibility:** Occupants share the responsibility for creating a successful cleaning program by communicating their needs and understanding the value of cleaning. Occupant activities can have serious consequences, even if they're unintentional. (The coffee stain that isn't reported immediately, for example, becomes a stain that requires more aggressive — and impactful — methods to be cleaned.) To achieve a healthy, high-performing building, each occupant has to be aware of her responsibility to others.

The overall goal of stewardship is to get everyone in the building involved in caring for the building. Chances are that workers spend almost as much time in their building as they do at home — why not demonstrate a similar level of concern and responsibility for its care?

Looking into the triple bottom line

Green cleaning is good for business. The potential impact on your bottom line is significant when you implement a green cleaning program. In fact, we define three bottom lines, collectively known as the *triple bottom line,* that a green cleaning program can positively impact. Like a three-legged stool, which needs three stable legs to function, keeping these three bottom lines in balance makes your program even more effective.

The three bottom lines are:

- ✔ **Economic:** The economic bottom line, or profitability, is measured in dollars and cents and tracks increased productivity, improvements in return on investment, energy savings, and so on. These are hard numbers and easy to measure.

- ✔ **Environmental:** In the United States, commercial and institutional cleaning is a $140 billion industry, annually consuming approximately 6 billion pounds of chemicals, 4.5 billion pounds of janitorial paper, and using a billion pounds of tools, equipment, and other supplies. The extraction of raw materials and manufacturing of these products have significant environmental impacts, as does their transportation, use, and disposal. Many of our raw materials are limited and nonrenewable, which means that once depleted, they're no longer available to future generations for their use.

- ✔ **Social:** For any enterprise to be sustainable, it must take care of its people. After all, how can a business succeed if it can't find workers? Or a university if faculty and students don't want to be there because the buildings are unhealthy? Or a city if people don't want to live there because the air is dirty and water unhealthy?

  Our industry hasn't traditionally considered the social impact of its activities. We can't expect people outside our industry to engage us as professionals or look at cleaning with respect unless and until we do. Part of that requires us to treat the people who perform the actual work with respect and dignity and to pay them a fair wage. In reality, this means looking at our industry in an entirely new way.

Exploring the social bottom line in depth is far beyond the scope of this book. We encourage you to join the conversations with your peers as they explore these issues. We sincerely hope that cleaning as an industry can move this forward before the government steps in with mandated wages and other regulations.

Spanning the green continuum

Think of a bar stretching from the left side of the page to the right and continuing right off the edge of the paper. At the far left, the bar is dark brown. As you move to the right, the brown begins to fade, becomes white, and then gradually becomes a light green. Continuing to the right the green slowly gets greener and brighter. There is no end as the bar continues right off the edge of the page.

This bar, the *green continuum,* represents the comparative nature of our definition of green. Any point to the right will be greener than a point to the left. The idea is that your green cleaning program is on that continuum. Wherever you are today is an improvement over some earlier point, and you have the opportunity to continue to improve and become greener.

Look at the green continuum as a gentle reminder that you don't have to do it all at once. As you develop your program, we encourage you to set realistic goals (certainly, you should stretch a bit) and continually evaluate your progress. As you evaluate new products, equipment, or procedures make sure they're moving you farther to the right on the green continuum. Green cleaning is a journey that continually strives to reduce health and evironmental impacts.

Who's Going Green?

Fifteen years ago when Steve published his first article on green cleaning, he stepped into virgin territory. The article focused on the EPA's new draft guidelines for purchasing environmentally preferred products. Actually getting the article placed was difficult as the whole "green thing" was thought to be a fad that would soon pass.

Steve didn't give up, and neither did green cleaning. These days, it's virtually impossible to pick up an issue of an industry magazine without finding an article about green cleaning. Articles about green buildings are commonplace in management and realty journals. Scientific research into the impacts of green building, daylighting, improved indoor environmental quality, and green cleaning has been conducted extensively over the past two decades.

Green cleaning isn't a fad, and it's not going away anytime soon. The number of buildings implementing green cleaning programs gets larger everyday. The following are examples of the growth of green cleaning:

✔ All federal agencies are mandated to green their cleaning programs (primarily by purchasing environmentally preferred chemicals), but many are taking an even more proactive approach.

  • Environmental Protection Agency's Region 2 Headquarters, a U.S. General Services Administration (GSA) building in New York City, was the site of the very first green cleaning program. Initiated in the mid-'90s, this was the forerunner of all subsequent federal green cleaning programs. EPA's Washington, D.C., headquarters is now converting to green cleaning.

  • U.S. Department of Interior (DOI) Headquarters initiated the first actual contract that included very specific requirements for a range of cleaning chemicals, paper, and liners. Additional green cleaning requirements included a stewardship plan.

✔ Many states have begun mandating the purchase and use of green cleaning chemicals, paper, and liners in their buildings, and some include specific requirements concerning green cleaning procedures. These states include Massachusetts, Minnesota, California, New York, Pennsylvania, Vermont, and Washington.

✔ Various counties and municipalities are also initiating green cleaning requirements for their facilities. Included in this growing list are Chicago, Illinois; New York, New York; King County, Washington; Phoenix, Arizona; Santa Monica, California; Alameda County, California; Austin, Texas; Minneapolis, Minnesota; and many, many more.

✔ In the private sector, the U.S. Green Building Council leads the movement for certifying green buildings. Founded in 1993, the USGBC sets green standards for buildings being designed and constructed as well as existing buildings that wish to make significant improvements in reducing their impact on health and the environment. You find more details about the USGBC, its members, and standards as well as several other organizations that support and promote green buildings and green cleaning, in the appendixes to this book.

✔ In the nonprofit advocacy sector, environmental and children's health groups such as the Healthy Schools Campaign, Hospitals for a Healthy Environment, Green Cleaning Network, and others are working with building sectors to encourage green cleaning.

Implementing a Green Cleaning Program

Sure, green cleaning sounds like a good idea, but how do you go about putting a green cleaning program in place? We're glad you asked. In this section, we give you an overview of how to proceed. We tell you more about each of these steps in later chapters. At this point, we're taking a look from the 25,000-foot level.

There are five basic steps to developing and implementing a green cleaning program:

1. **Get everyone on board.**

   Getting to an agreement involves two key issues:

   - Making sure the key stakeholders agree that they want a green cleaning program.

   - Getting agreement as to what a green cleaning program is. Simply put, we're talking about expectation management.

   We give you tips for accomplishing both missions in Chapter 4. After you reach agreement, you need to build your green team — the people who will be responsible for developing and implementing the green cleaning plan.

2. **Establish the baseline and build a plan.**

   Implementing a green cleaning program is a journey. Like any other journey, you have a better chance of getting where you want to go if you have a map. And maps need starting points. To find your baseline, your team conducts a number of facility and housekeeping surveys.

   Analyze the information your team collects and look for the best opportunities for improvement. We take you through this process in Chapter 5.

3. **Developing green cleaning procedures and training plans.**

   Green cleaning procedures focus on cleaning effectiveness and aren't significantly different from traditional cleaning systems. Making procedures green focuses on reducing custodians' and building occupants' exposures to harmful contaminants, reducing waste and environmental impacts, and making processes more efficient.

   As with cleaning procedures, the training programs you use in your green cleaning program are similar to traditional training programs. You don't have to reinvent the wheel, but you do want to make sure that everyone is up to speed with your procedures. We outline procedures and training in Chapter 6.

4. Build your green toolbox.

Green cleaning is more than changing products. Throughout this book, we show you that green cleaning is a holistic approach to caring for a building. However, green cleaning does include choosing the right tools for the job. That means examining and changing the chemicals, equipment, paper, liners, mats, and other supplies you use to care for the building to move further to the right on the green continuum.

We cover the green toolbox in much more detail in Part III.

5. Create communication and stewardship plans.

With change come expectations — high and low — and your program gets off to its strongest start when you develop a communication plan that manages expectations and shows off your successes. Furthermore, to be a part of caring for the building, occupants need to know what is happening, how it affects them, what their roles and responsibilities are, and when and how they're supposed to carry them out. This is another key component of your communications plan. We discuss communication in Chapter 9.

To keep your program strong and to ensure that it continually improves, you need to create a stewardship plan. Chapter 8 tells you about this plan in great detail. The stewardship plan formalizes the concept of shared responsibility, which is a prerequisite to making your green cleaning program sustainable.

Does Green Cleaning Cost More than Traditional Cleaning?

This complex question deserves a careful answer. First, though, we'd like to make a few blunt statements to appropriately set the stage for our answer to this question:

✔ Cost reduction is *not* a goal of green cleaning programs.

✔ We believe that the average level of cleaning in commercial and institutional buildings is less than adequate today. This is not because cleaning professionals don't know how to clean; it is primarily due to not being given the opportunity to do what needs to be done.

> ✔ Our society doesn't place an appropriate value on cleaning and its impact on health and the environment, and neither does it properly value the people who perform these tasks.

With those points in mind, we return to the cost question. First consider the cost of cleaning products, equipment, paper, and supplies.

Today, every major cleaning chemical manufacturer offers a line of green products. Some more, some less, but finding these products has become easier than just a few years ago. Five or ten years ago, green cleaning chemicals either cost more or didn't work as well as their traditional counterparts. But today, because of the competitive nature of the marketplace, accelerating sales and manufacturing volumes, and improved technologies, most green cleaning chemicals are priced at levels competitive with traditional products.

In the equipment arena, the situation is similar. A particular piece of green equipment may carry a price tag slightly steeper than a more traditional version. However, that increase is usually more than offset by its durability, which extends the replacement cycle and ultimate cost of the product, as well as improvements in efficiency with labor and chemical cost savings.

When comparing green janitorial paper products, you find more variety in pricing. Although some lines are quite competitive with traditional paper products, others are still priced at premium levels. The difference represents an imbalance between capacity and demand. As demand for the green versions increases, production will increase and prices will fall. Meanwhile, some interesting developments in the non-tree-based paper products are occurring. These may offer exciting green alternatives at extremely competitive prices.

The question of cost becomes much more difficult to analyze when you start looking at procedures and labor costs. At the most basic level, if the basic cleaning being performed today is adequate and no significant changes are made beyond changing to greener chemicals, equipment, and paper products, the overall cost impact is probably neutral.

However, if current cleaning frequencies or intensities aren't adequate for properly maintaining the building, and you make changes to meet the needs of the occupants, the cost of cleaning increases because cleaning frequencies and labor costs increase. But take a look at whether this cost increase is because of a green cleaning program or merely a reflection of the cost of creating an adequate cleaning program. We believe it's the latter.

Finally, consider the implications of implementing a full-scale green cleaning program. Not only will you change some products and equipment, but you'll examine and modify the cleaning specifications and procedures to deliver a Class A cleaning service. You'll implement an effective employee training and development program, offering a wage and benefit package commensurate with the increased skill levels. You'll develop and implement an extensive communication program and charter a stewardship team to ensure your program is sustainable.

Clearly this new program will cost substantially more than the program it replaces. Consider, though, what might happen after the new program is implemented:

- Occupant productivity increases 1 to 2 percent.

- Energy and water costs are reduced 10 to 20 percent.

- Tenant complaints drop by more than 40 percent.

- Tenant retention increases and vacancy rates are at record lows.

- Turnover within the cleaning staff drops from 150 percent to 10 percent, saving hiring and training costs.

- Cleaning equipment replacement costs drop more than 90 percent because you're using better-made products.

- The recycling program generates several thousands of dollars, creating a new profit center in the facility.

- Workers' compensation claims in the maintenance department drop significantly, and you don't lose days because of injury.

- The carpet-spotting program, combined with spill kits at all coffee stations, allows planned carpet replacement costs to be delayed two to three years.

- Elimination of corrosive chemicals prevents damage to restroom fixtures, reducing replacement costs and plumbing contractor calls.

- Standardizing trash cans and liner sizes saves $2,000 per year in liner costs.

- Replacing multifold hand towels with large roll towels dispensed from touch-free dispensers reduces paper consumption by 30 percent and saves $2,000 per year in paper costs.

Of course, in the "real world," the costs and benefits are charged or posted to a variety of different departments and no one ever sees the roll-up. So the green cleaning program is cancelled as an expensive experiment and a few clueless managers get bonuses for their cost-savings efforts. Unless . . .

Unless you have a stewardship team (see Chapter 8) who measures and compares these costs and benefits. A team who "gets it," understanding the answers to the questions we asked at the beginning of this chapter and who keeps the benefits of your program in constant focus.

Is It Your Time to Go Green?

Change is hard. First you have to discover the new way of doing things, and you probably can't take time away from your normal responsibilities as you find out about new concepts, terms, standards, regulations, and so on. Then you have to undertake consensus building, team building, planning, follow-up, measurement, and so on. Yes, change *is* hard.

And then there's the rest of your organization. Few organizations (in truth, we've never heard of *one*) embrace change, regardless of what their vision or mission statements say. Organizations are made up of people, and human nature craves stability. So, even after you've done your homework, built your plans, and put all the pieces into place you still have to herd a bunch of stability-seeking, change-phobic human beings in this new direction.

Is all this effort really worth it? You might guess that we think it is — after all we've written a book to help you do it. In Chapter 2, we explore the impacts cleaning has on health, productivity, profitability, and the environment. After you've worked your way through that chapter, we hope (and believe) you'll agree that green cleaning *is* important. But make no mistake, success depends on your commitment and willingness to work through many of the hard parts to come.

Chapter 2

Why Is Green Cleaning Important?

*G*reen cleaning, in a nutshell, is an approach to cleaning that protects the health of people without harming the environment. When you implement a green cleaning program, you're *simultaneously* protecting human health and the environment.

Green cleaning isn't a product and has no end. Instead, it's a concept that ultimately focuses on creating the healthiest, highest-performing indoor environment that meets the unique needs of building occupants and reduces impacts on the outdoor environment.

Many people think of implementing a green cleaning program as embarking on a journey. You're improving the current situation and continually improving into the future.

Like all maintenance activities, cleaning often is seen as simply an expense. And, like most expenses, the goal has been cost reduction, often through reduction or elimination of services. Cleaning for "acceptable appearance" or "minimal occupant complaints" has been the accepted standard in the traditional cleaning model. Yet cleaning has a tremendous impact on the overall performance of the facility as well as its occupants. The products, equipment, and processes you employ can have positive and negative impacts.

Poor cleaning impacts the life cycle of surfaces such as carpet, tile, walls, and fixtures. Without proper maintenance with appropriate products and procedures, surfaces may be damaged. Over time, the useful life of that item may be substantially reduced.

You also find a direct correlation between the quality of cleaning and the number of building occupant complaints you receive. From missed trash cans to carpet spots, dirt in corners to smelly restrooms, inadequate cleaning can lead to scores of complaints. However, you may not be as aware of the impact poor cleaning has on occupant productivity, health, morale, and objective measures such as student test scores or attendance.

As the following sections outline, paying closer attention to the products and procedures rewards you and your team in several important ways.

Improving Indoor Air Quality

Cleaning is incredibly important in protecting a building — structural materials, furnishings, mechanical and climate control systems, equipment such as computers, and other property. Poor cleaning can lead to shorter-than-expected life cycles, expensive repair requirements, or high replacement costs.

Cleaning is also essential to creating a safe, healthy, and productive work and living space for the building's occupants. People spend as much as 90 percent of their time indoors, and some people, such as those in health care and military facilities, may spend 100 percent of their time indoors for extended periods.

The United States Environmental Protection Agency estimates that the indoor air may be two to five times as polluted as the air outside, and its Science Advisory Board has consistently placed indoor air quality among the top five most important environmental issues.

Indoor air pollutants include the dirt, dust, and other contaminants people bring in from outside. Pollution also includes dust generated from our indoor activities, gasses released from furniture and building materials, the germs we spread as we touch things or cough and sneeze, and the products we use to clean and maintain the building.

Unfortunately, by focusing cleaning efforts on achieving an acceptable appearance, the traditional cleaning program may do little to address these issues. Because a green cleaning program *begins* with the goal of protecting health and the environment, the choices of products, equipment, and procedures are specifically designed to address the issues we identify in this section. As an additional benefit, a green cleaning program delivers an excellent appearance as well!

Many cleaning chemicals are powerful and can be hazardous not only to the person using them, but to the rest of the building population. For example, toxic pest elimination chemicals can linger in the indoor environment and therefore be inhaled or ingested. Even the healthiest individuals can be impacted by inhaling or ingesting these chemicals, but doing so is of particular concern for people with impaired immune systems, pregnant women, children, and the elderly.

Cleaning's Impact in Office Buildings

The most common intended impact of cleaning in an office building is to improve or maintain acceptable appearance levels. Cleaning's impact is felt in many not-so-obvious ways, as well. Consider three major concerns of building owners and managers: productivity, litigation, and marketing. Each of these concerns impacts the organization's bottom line. What do they have to do with cleaning? Glad you asked! Read on to see how these interests play into a typical commercial office environment.

Productivity

Building Related Illness or BRI (an indoor environment that actually causes illness in building occupants because of the contaminants they're exposed to) affects many American workers. Those afflicted experience respiratory complaints, asthma, and allergies. Many people confuse BRI with Sick Building Syndrome (SBS), which causes a general malaise without an identifiable, specific cause. Traditionally, these types of complaints show up as sick days, doctor visits, and decreased productivity measures. The economic impact of BRI and SBS is staggering and adds up to billions of dollars in lost productivity.

Improving the indoor environmental quality fights both BRI and SBS and therefore improves productivity and saves companies money.

Many experts agree that a 2 percent increase in worker productivity is about average when a building implements effective improvements to the indoor environment. The cost of worker salary and benefits in a typical Class A office building is about $130 per square foot. Just a 1 percent improvement in productivity could yield a savings of $1.30 per square foot — about what is spent in that facility for all cleaning operations on an annual basis. In other words, a modest improvement in productivity arising from improved indoor environmental quality because of a green cleaning program can more than pay for itself almost immediately.

Litigation

Because people spend so much time indoors, the impact of indoor environmental quality on their health, productivity, and comfort can be dramatic. Litigation relating to indoor air quality, Sick Building Syndrome, mold, and other problems has increased dramatically in just the past few years. The potential for more lawsuits as reports of problems associated with poor indoor air quality is staggering, especially in public buildings.

Even if cases are settled without going to court, the costs associated with this litigation are enormous, often eclipsing the profits associated with managing an otherwise profitable facility. A green cleaning program coupled with an effective communication plan can be a powerful tool in preventing this type of litigation. Properly and effectively communicating the goals, process, and successes of your program allays many fears and helps occupants recognize the positive impacts of your program.

Marketing

Poor cleaning of any kind generates complaints. Who wouldn't prefer to work in a cleaner, healthier facility? The already-high cost of replacing a tenant is climbing. The leasing market is very competitive; marketing costs to attract new tenants far outweigh any investments required to improve the cleaning operation for current tenants. The costs associated with remodeling the facility to suit the new tenant are another factor. The advantages of retaining current tenants can't be overstated, and a green cleaning program, which costs little to implement, goes a long way toward keeping tenants.

Owners and managers are looking for every edge possible to attract and hold profitable tenants. Although cleaning has often been looked at as simply an expense, an effective green cleaning program can be used as a powerful tool in this competitive marketplace. In fact, as general awareness of the advantages offered by a healthier workplace grows, companies that seek office space are looking for buildings that have demonstrated their awareness of these issues.

Many companies have embraced the concepts of sustainability and stewardship; they're promoting their efforts to reduce their impact on the environment and create healthier, safer workplaces. These companies have also found that incorporating a green mission is a powerful marketing tool.

Cleaning's Impact on Schools

Children are more vulnerable to contaminants in the environment as a result of poor cleaning and to the dangers of harsh or toxic chemicals. Pound for pound, children eat more food, drink more liquids, and breathe more air than adults. Furthermore, their immune systems aren't as developed as an adult's, and their breathing rate tends to be much faster, allowing the inhalation of even more contaminants.

Children's vulnerability shows up as a skyrocketing increase in the asthma rate, increasing rates of childhood cancer, increasing behavioral and attention deficit disorders — some of which are attributed to contaminants from their environment.

In schools the evidence is clear: Study after study demonstrates the impact of cleaning and indoor environmental quality on students' health, performance, attendance, and test scores. Asthma and allergic reactions have reached levels so alarming that they're regularly reported in major newspapers.

In the past decade, school buildings have evolved to be more than the places children go to learn to read and write. The facilities are being used for public meetings, community gatherings, churches, and more. Instead of a building that shuts down at 5 p.m., today's schools are used 15 to 20 hours a day, often six or seven days per week.

At the same time, school districts are faced with unprecedented budget cuts. Rather than building new facilities or expanding current buildings, districts are increasing class sizes or using non-classroom space for teaching, crowding more students into already overcrowded facilities. Larger class sizes aren't only difficult for teachers to handle, but provide increased opportunities for transmitting germs and illness among the occupants.

Too often the administration looks at cleaning as an expendable service because the cleaning industry has failed to help it understand the connection between cleaning and learning, which is the primary mission of the school.

As demands on the facilities continue to grow, the staff assigned to clean and maintain them has been cut. Just as in a commercial setting, the impact of poor cleaning results in increased facility costs — repairs, unplanned replacement costs, and remedial measures to correct problems.

The impact on the health and productivity of students and staff is equally dramatic. Increased visits to the school nurse, absenteeism, and poor test results are all related to poor indoor environmental quality. A properly planned and monitored green cleaning program can not only improve the health and performance of the school's students and staff, but can provide a high level of control and predictability over the maintenance budget.

The positive impact improvements in cleaning practices can have on learning is dramatic.

Cleaning's Impact on Health Care

The potential impacts of cleaning in the health care industry are enormous. Consider the scope of this industry:

- ✔ There are more than 660,000 patients in our hospitals every day
- ✔ Full Time Equivalent staff (FTE) numbers more than 4.5 million
- ✔ More than 100,000 trainees and volunteers are working in the hospitals
- ✔ Millions of people visit every day
- ✔ There are 3,350,000 residents of long-term care facilities
- ✔ And more than 2,000,000 FTE staff caring for them

By definition, a patient in the hospital is in a vulnerable condition, often with a weaker immune system than the average person. This makes them more susceptible to environmental irritants and pollutants than most of us. Yet, because they're indoors 24 hours a day, isolating them from the cleaning activities going on around them is virtually impossible.

Even healthy staff members are constantly exposed to a variety of germs and pathogens not found in the "normal" environment. This places them at greater risk to additional contaminants than they would be in an office facility or at home.

Products, processes, and procedures that would be mildly irritating to an average, healthy person can be potentially life threatening to someone with a weakened immune system. However, most general cleaning procedures carried out in hospitals don't vary from those used in general office cleaning. Although the health care industry practices a high level of cleaning in critical care areas, it isn't immune to the problems associated with typical cleaning standards.

An even larger problem lurks in the health care industry. Every year more than 2 million people contract a *nosocomial infection,* an infection or illness acquired in the hospital. Each year, more than 70,000 people (9 every hour) die in the United States as a result of a nosocomial infection. To put that in perspective, consider these statistics:

- ✔ 50,000 die in automobile accidents

- ✔ 7,000 drown

- ✔ 5,000 die of burns

Many nosocomial infections can be traced to inadequate general cleaning practices, contaminated surfaces, and poor dust control, but laying the bulk of the blame at the feet of the cleaning industry would be wrong. Nonetheless, several studies indicate that implementing and following an effective hand-washing program could cut the rate of nosocomial infections in half!

Organizations such as Hospitals for a Healthy Environment are working to improve the cleaning standards of the industry while minimizing the negative impacts on patients, staff, and the environment. (See the appendixes for more information about these organizations.) The opportunities to create a positive impact in the health care industry through the implementation of an effective green cleaning program are significant. Some of these include:

- ✔ Reducing exposure of vulnerable patients to potentially dangerous chemicals.

- ✔ Modifying procedures to reduce exposures to cross contamination by using a microfiber cloth cleaning system that replaces the cloths in each new area to be cleaned.

- ✔ Addressing the issue of nosocomial infections by installing effective, easy-to-use hand-washing stations.

- ✔ Implementing a sustainable floor-care system that eliminates the need for burnishing. This reduces the dust (and contaminants that hitch a ride on dust particles) kicked into the air-handling system.

- ✔ Increasing awareness of potential negative impacts from overusing disinfectants and implementing an effective program that uses the proper disinfectant only where actually required.

Cleaning's Impact on the Cleaning Industry

The cleaning industry is one of the largest employers in our country, with more than 3.5 million custodians. Consider the turnover in the industry (estimated at more than 200 percent in some segments), and that number climbs significantly. Any impact on the industry affects a tremendous number of people.

The way we have traditionally approached cleaning has a financial and social impact on the people who do the cleaning. (Check out Chapter 1 to find out more.) Green cleaning itself can't completely resolve these issues, but increased focus on training and professionalism helps move the perception of cleaning upward.

The products and procedures involved in cleaning impact the health and well-being of the people who perform these services, as well. Exposure to potentially toxic or caustic materials can result in burns and other serious injuries. Incidences of work-related asthma are increasing dramatically. And musculoskeletal injuries are increasing every year. More than 6 percent of the people involved in providing cleaning services suffer on-the-job injuries annually. You see the financial impacts in escalating workers' compensation rates.

And it's not just cleaning chemicals that cause injuries. Equipment that isn't ergonomically designed or isn't matched to the size or capabilities of the operator contribute to musculoskeletal injuries. Even well-designed equipment causes problems if the operator isn't trained to use it properly or safely.

Two tremendous costs are rampant in the cleaning industry:

- *Workers' compensation,* insurance for employees injured on the job, is often cited as the single highest cost associated with providing cleaning services after the cost of labor itself. The typical cost to an employer for a work-related injury is $625. Considering that janitorial work is often part time and usually offers a low wage, the financial impact to the employee for missing work can be extremely significant.

  Efforts to provide safer products, ergonomic equipment, proper training, and a good working environment can show a demonstrated and documented payback in a relatively short period of time.

- *Turnover rates* are high in the cleaning industry; more than 200 percent in some segments. In any business, working conditions and the tools provided to accomplish the job are a significant factor in employee satisfaction and productivity.

> If equipment doesn't work, is hard to use, or causes pain or injury, an employee is less likely to stay on the job. If the chemicals used to clean cause injury or discomfort, an employee is more likely to look for employment elsewhere. If an employee is confused, can't get training, or feels like he can't do a good job, he is more likely to leave.

A properly designed green cleaning program

✔ Uses safer chemicals, portion-control dispensers, and pre-measured pouches to protect users from concentrated products

✔ Stresses the importance of ergonomically designed backpack vacuums and other equipment that is more comfortable and safer to use

✔ Trains employees in the proper procedures and use of chemicals and equipment

These elements directly impact turnover and workers' compensation. For a building-service contractor, this can lead to increased profitability; for in-house operations, it means more tasks can be completed with existing staff, meeting budgets and possibly avoiding outsourcing.

Cleaning's Impact on the Environment

The impact the cleaning industry has on the environment is significant. The following sections run down some of the ways cleaning affects the environment.

A well-designed, well-implemented, and well-monitored green cleaning program addresses all of these issues, improving the quality of our indoor environment while minimizing potential adverse effects on health and the environment as a whole.

Cleaning chemicals

Every year approximately 6 billion pounds of chemicals are used by the cleaning industry. Add in the raw materials and processes used to produce them, and that number is increased by a factor of 10, becoming 60 billion pounds annually.

Certainly these products are important to accomplish our tasks of protecting the health of occupants and the buildings themselves. But some of these chemicals are hazardous and can cause serious environmental damage. Furthermore, most of these products are made from nonrenewable natural resources such as petroleum (which, once it is depleted, isn't available to be used by future generations). Given the huge numbers involved, and the potential impact on health and the environment, choosing and using chemicals appropriately is critical. For info on choosing green chemicals, see Chapter 10.

Janitorial paper

More than 4.5 billion pounds of janitorial paper are consumed each year in commercial and institutional buildings. Janitorial paper includes toilet and facial tissue, hand towels, wipes, and so on. The bulk of janitorial paper is still made from virgin tree pulp and requires the cutting of approximately 27 million trees each year.

People are accustomed to using tissue and hand towels that are bleached a bright white. During production, this paper is often bleached with chlorine compounds, releasing toxins such as dioxin into the environment. Dioxins are carcinogenic and considered some of the most deadly man-made substances on earth. For more on paper, see Chapter 12.

Equipment

More than 1 billion pounds of vacuum cleaners and other powered equipment, buckets, trash cans, carts, and other supplies, tools, and equipment are produced every year, consuming large quantities of natural resources and energy. Many of these were designed to be extremely inexpensive and sold to be disposable. They were made with inferior components, intended to be abused and discarded. The disposal of these older materials would fill approximately 20,000 tractor trailers, making a sizable and nonbiodegradable impact on our landfills, while the environmental impacts from the production of replacement materials contribute more environmental burdens and unnecessary costs. For more on this, see Chapter 11.

Trash can liners

Americans consume more than 35 billion plastic trash can liners every year. That's 95 million bags every day! And unfortunately they're often too thin and require double bagging, or they're too large for the containers and waste plastic materials. Some progress has been made in creating bags from recycled content or using natural materials like corn, but the vast majority of these are made from virgin plastic — raw, nonrenewable petroleum.

Chapter 3

Green Cleaning for Specific Situations

The principles of a green cleaning program are similar across the broad spectrum of situations in which they're implemented, but the different populations, priorities, and unique challenges within each type of organization can influence how you implement a successful program.

In this chapter, we look at the specifics of green cleaning programs in office buildings, schools, health care facilities, and for building service contractors.

Implementing Green Cleaning in Office Buildings

Within the office-building category, you find a wide range of facilities — from single, owner-occupied and -managed buildings to sprawling multi-tenant campuses operated by national management companies and serviced by multiple building service contractors. They may be limited to typical white collar office occupants or may include retail shops, small manufacturing or production areas, day care centers, and a variety of other businesses. Finally, they may fall completely in the private sector, public sector (government offices), or include some of each.

Each of these may have many unique variables that could ultimately impact your efforts in implementing a green cleaning program in some way. Exploring all of these differences would require a book much larger than this one. The good news is that not all of these differences are equally significant, and we divide this category into just a few representative segments. We pick out the most significant features of each and provide the basic information you need to help implement the program in your organization.

Owner-occupied and -managed facilities

An owner-occupied and -managed office building is the most straightforward — typically it's a single-use facility, and the owner can make a decision and cause it to be implemented.

About the only common denominator within the population of virtually any office building is adulthood. Beyond that, you're likely to find a mix of healthy occupants and people with various illnesses, sensitivities, and vulnerabilities.

The advantage in an owner-occupied and -managed building is that identifying and accommodating occupants with special needs may be easier and more straightforward.

Occupant — and in this case employee — productivity and performance is probably the most significant goal for implementing a green cleaning program in a single tenant or owner-occupied building. Following closely is the desire to control cleaning and maintenance costs. Note however, we say *controlling* costs — not necessarily reducing cleaning costs, because in some buildings the level of cleaning should be increased to create a healthy, high-performing building, and that may create an increase in cost.

Green cleaning also feeds into an owner's marketing goals because it can be used to demonstrate her commitment to sustainability, corporate responsibility, and other initiatives. A healthier facility also can be an effective incentive when looking for new employees.

 Every building and combination of occupants is unique. You may have to address a "problem" building, one that has unusual levels of various pollutants or irritants, where there have been excessive cases of *Building Related Illness* (an indoor environment that actually causes illness in building occupants because of the contaminants they're exposed to) or the building design doesn't allow for adequate ventilation. It may be a high-profile facility or historic landmark. The list of potential unique challenges is extensive. The key point to bear in mind here is that *whatever* set of unique challenges apply to your facility or organization, you need to identify them *before* beginning to plan your green cleaning program.

Multi-tenant office buildings

Although the bulk of a multi-tenant building may be made up of offices, they may share the facility with print shops, small retail stores, day care centers, coffee shops, nail and hair salons, and other types of businesses. Your green cleaning plan must recognize and properly address the potential impacts these types of operations have on the total facility.

These buildings are usually managed by professional management companies, but they may be managed by an owner or owner-occupant, as well. In either case, there are some important differences between these kinds of facilities and the single-tenant or owner-occupied buildings we discuss in the previous section:

✔ You find a diverse population of occupants; however, identifying vulnerable occupants that might benefit from a modification of cleaning in their space may be complex. Tenant companies may not be willing (or able) to help you gather the information you need.

  During your building audit (see Chapter 5), be sure to look for clues such as individual space heaters and air filters, diverters taped to HVAC ducts, and personal cleaning supplies near desks. These are often very telling indicators that signal someone who is bothered by the conditions in their area.

✔ Goals for this kind of building usually include the desire to create a healthier building as part of the effort to attract and retain tenants or avoid potential litigation.

  One of the most common reasons for implementing a green cleaning program in a multi-tenant building is responding to a major tenant who has decided to go green.

✔ Challenges that arise frequently in these facilities include the desire of a major tenant to influence or even lead the efforts to improve the indoor environment. Clearly understanding their overall objectives is essential so that you can try to address them in your plan.

✔ Communication can be a major challenge because there may not be a single vehicle for posting information (such as an internal intranet or company newsletter) to communicate to all building occupants and visitors. Meet with the individual tenant representatives to discuss the benefits of communicating with their employees and determine which communication tools would work best for them. Chapter 9 tells you more about communicating effectively.

What about protecting the environment?

As we discuss the various green cleaning goals in each type of organization, we hardly mention protecting the environment. Does this mean it isn't a viable goal? Or that we don't believe these organizations would have this as a goal? Of course not. In fact, we believe many organizations will place that goal near the top of their list. We chose to pull this goal out separately to make a point.

You don't have to be a tree-hugger or even consider yourself environmentally aware to find significant benefits to green cleaning. As we show you in Chapter 2, the benefits to productivity, cost savings by reducing health-care issues, and return on investment make an extremely compelling business case for implementing a green cleaning program.

On the other hand, many people who don't consider themselves to be environmentalists might be surprised to consider the impact cleaning has on the things they do enjoy. The wonderful thing about green cleaning is that you really can do well by doing good.

When you make changes, people *will* notice. If you don't offer an explanation for those changes, the natural inclination is to assume that something was wrong and you've finally fixed it — just the opposite of what you want people to think.

Government facilities and tenants

Governments at all levels have begun to enact specific executive orders, mandates, laws, and regulations covering how their facilities are to be cleaned and what products can be used to clean them.

In many cases, you find that their green cleaning specifications focus on product and equipment selection. Very few have yet to look at procedures, training, and other issues. In other words, if you're already developing comprehensive green cleaning programs, the regulations are simply a subset of your normal operations and quite easy to absorb into your program. If you haven't yet gone green — or if this is your first effort — for the most part, you can easily meet the government's requirements by following the advice in this book.

Existing (nongreen) cleaning specifications in government facilities tend to be very detailed and rigidly scheduled. Quite often, these schedules have little to do with the actual conditions or needs of the facility. Usually the cleaning contractor is evaluated on meeting the schedule, with payments deducted for missing a scheduled event (whether the work was actually needed or not). Conflict arises as you develop a unique cleaning plan for a specific building. One of the keys to green cleaning is doing only the necessary tasks and skipping those that would waste time and chemicals or expose occupants to activities that aren't necessary.

In some cases, you may be able to work with a contracting officer or property manager to implement a performance-based cleaning program and make the necessary changes to the specifications and bring the entire program into line. In others, you may simply have to wait until practical considerations catch up to regulations.

Implementing Green Cleaning in Schools

School might mean an inner-city grade school, a suburban high school, a small private college campus, or a large state university. To keep our discussion manageable we divide this category into K-12 schools (kindergarten through senior high school) and universities. We also highlight differences between private and publicly funded schools in each category.

K-12 schools

Public schools have undergone some significant changes in the past two decades. In simpler times, the local school had plenty of room for students and staff and except for school plays and sports events was closed by five o'clock at night. Today, thousands of students are jammed into buildings designed to hold half that number. And the school has become an extension of the community, serving breakfasts and hosting meetings and special nonschool events — even church services. It isn't unusual to find schools with activities scheduled six or seven days a week from early morning until after 10 or 11 p.m.

As you plan and implement a green cleaning program for schools, make sure you understand what these other uses are. They may introduce contaminants into the facility that your plan will have to deal with. Focusing only on what happens between 8 a.m. and 3 p.m. may cause you to miss very important details that impact the success of your program.

The impact of budget cuts has been felt in almost every school district and most acutely in building and grounds departments. It's relatively easy to demonstrate the connection between class size and student learning. The link between a clean, healthy facility and learning hasn't been demonstrated to the general public as effectively.

However, studies *have* identified a connection between how a school is maintained and students' ability to learn. Society needs to understand this connection and assign it a proper value. As a professional in the cleaning industry, you can help make that happen and it is imperative that you do so.

The students present a whole new set of challenges:

- ✔ They are more vulnerable than adults. Their respiration rates are significantly higher than those of adults, meaning they draw potential irritants and pollutants into their lungs at twice the rate of an adult.

- ✔ Because they're much smaller than adults, children are subject to a greater impact of irritants. What might be a simple irritant to a healthy adult may be harmful to a child.

- ✔ Children's rapidly developing bodies and immune systems put them at greater risk of harm than adults.

- ✔ Students often come to school with colds, flu, and a variety of respiratory and other illnesses.

- ✔ In many cases, students have inadequate diets or are exposed to other environmental dangers, making them even more vulnerable in the crowded school environment.

- ✔ Public schools are required to mainstream special-needs students. Many of these children are extremely vulnerable to environmental contaminants — normally occurring dusts, pollens, spores, and so on — and the impacts of cleaning products and procedures.

The situation in most private schools is better. The students typically come from more affluent families and have access to better diets and health care. Private schools tend to be less crowded (whether by limiting admissions or because of high tuition costs) and maintenance tends to be better as well. However, cleaning and maintenance is usually focused on appearance rather than cleaning for health. The opportunities for greening private schools are just as real as for public schools.

Green cleaning goals

The overarching goal is to provide a safer, healthier environment for students and staff that promotes effective learning. Given the fiscal requirements of most communities, controlling costs is also very important.

Demonstrate the connection between a healthy school and improved learning, reduced absenteeism, and better test scores. Doing so can help you make a case for reversing budget cuts. A significant portion of funding is related directly to students being in school. Demonstrate that an effective green cleaning program can positively impact attendance, and you may be in a position to justify a reasonable budget increase.

One of the most telling impacts of budget cuts has been in purchasing cleaning supplies. If you look in the janitor closet of almost any typical school today you probably find old equipment in poor repair and a few bottles of bleach. Trying to clean a school with these supplies is not only difficult, it's dangerous. Investments in this area not only result in a healthier learning environment but can result in reduced risks and labor savings — and the ability to use that labor to accomplish more tasks.

In private schools, cleaning for appearance has long been part of presenting the school in a positive light to parents considering enrolling their children. Positioning the school as green can also be a very effective marketing tool.

Building the green team

In a school environment, you find a number of unique stakeholders who should be represented on the team:

- ✔ School nurse
- ✔ Attendance officer
- ✔ Indoor air quality (IAQ) coordinator
- ✔ School board members
- ✔ Parents
- ✔ Students
- ✔ Union officials
- ✔ Advocacy groups

Parent involvement is very important but can be difficult to get. By involving parents in your efforts you gain access and advocates for your cause as funding issues are debated and voted on in the community.

Union officials are important because they control implementation of many of your changes. Making sure that the unions not only understand but endorse your efforts will make implementation significantly easier and can spell the difference between success and failure.

Advocacy groups like the Parent Teacher Association (PTA) help you reach parents. Those organized specifically to help improve the health and well-being of students (Healthy Schools Campaign, for example) are an excellent resource for information, support, and guidance as you implement your plan. We highlight several in the appendixes of this book.

Unique challenges

Of the several challenges you face when implementing a green cleaning program in a school, the way public schools are funded may be the most significant. As the various stakeholders fight over an ever-shrinking financial pie, cleaning and maintenance is usually earmarked for cuts or at least no increases. Your success depends in large part on your ability to communicate the incredible importance of cleaning and green cleaning.

The second unique challenge is in dealing with unions. A union's goal is to protect its membership. Help them see the value of your proposal to their cause by showing them how green cleaning chemicals, equipment, and supplies reduce risk of injury.

Union representatives who have gone through "improvement projects" previously are likely to be concerned that your program is designed to cut labor costs or jobs, or to make their members work harder for less pay. Explain that any labor efficiencies allow additional tasks to be completed and often reduce the need for outside contractors. The teacher and staff unions need to understand the impact of cleaning on their members' health.

A final challenge is inertia. School janitors tend to have good job security and have been in their positions for many, many years. Practices are passed from the "old hand" to the new employee. Budget restrictions prevent travel to trade shows or outside training, reducing exposure to new ideas. You may hear that the crew uses bleach as a daily cleaner because they've always done it that way and it's always worked before.

The products and procedures you are introducing are likely to be very different from those that have been used for the past 25 years. Change is difficult, and even more so in this environment. Be sure to allow for ample communication beyond training to help get the custodians on board.

Colleges and universities

The situation in our colleges and universities is somewhat better than elementary and high schools. Generally, there is less crowding, buildings are not "overused" to the same extent, and the financial situation is a bit brighter. Unfortunately, this doesn't translate to an understanding of the impacts of cleaning or the value of green cleaning. Here are some further characteristics of colleges and universities:

✔ The population of colleges and universities is more like that of a typical office complex than a grade school — you're dealing with young adults and adults rather than young children. However, the population is as diverse in health issues, resistance to contaminants, and other vulnerabilities as any collection of adults. Because students typically move from classroom to classroom or building to building, isolating vulnerable populations becomes impossible.

✔ Most buildings on a campus are used for the activities they were designed to be used for. This makes maintenance tasks a bit easier to schedule and control. Naturally, you do find exceptions. Identify and allow for them in your plan.

✔ Creating a safe and healthy learning environment is the primary goal. However, in these facilities, whether public or private, marketing is a key goal as well. Unlike K-12 schools, which most children are required by law to attend, college is voluntary. As public perception of green cleaning improves and the connection between a healthy environment and learning is better understood by the public, green cleaning becomes an increasingly important point of distinction when recruiting new students and for demonstrating leadership and stewardship, especially in public institutions.

✔ Many colleges and universities have established green programs (whether they are part of sustainability initiative, building a new LEED-certified building, or other existing environmental effort), which are great places to find supporters who have already laid the groundwork for green cleaning.

✔ Colleges are a fertile ground for new trends. Identifying and nurturing student groups that are concerned with the environment, social ideals, and health issues can pay big dividends. These students are your ambassadors to the student body at large and help generate positive attention for your efforts.

Among the challenges of instituting a green cleaning program in a university setting are the following:

✔ Most colleges are a collection of buildings and can include classrooms, offices, health facilities, athletic facilities, residence halls, dining facilities, laboratories, and more — each requiring a specific cleaning strategy. In addition, the campus may include a wide variety of buildings ranging in age from newly built to 100 or more years old. Some may be in virtually new condition while others have suffered years of benign neglect. Your audit must note these variations and your plan account for them, including what should be done to bring the poorly maintained buildings into good repair.

✔ In many, if not most, colleges and universities the often small staff of professional custodians is augmented by students on a work-study program. Certainly these students can be effective custodians, but their reason for being in school is *not* to clean. They're there to learn and earn a degree. Conflicts between class schedules or tests and their job are usually resolved in favor of school.

This group tends to turn over quite a bit and training is often limited to an on-the-job walk-through. The key to success here is designing a training program that can be delivered quickly and efficiently. The program can be supported with on-the-job training, but the basic instruction needs to respect the student focus and available time. A series of short training presentations can be much more effective than a single one- or two-hour class.

Implementing Green Cleaning in Health Care Facilities

You might think that the one facility that would embrace green cleaning would be health care. After all, the mission of these facilities is to improve the health of its clients and *do no harm*. Unfortunately, the connection between cleaning and health, as well as cleaning's impact on the environment, isn't well understood in this realm, either. Nor is this segment any more immune to budget cuts and understaffing than others.

By definition, most of the population in health care facilities is vulnerable. Illness makes people more susceptible to environmental contaminants and the impacts of cleaning. Hospital patients who are confined to their beds are difficult if not impossible to isolate from the cleaning activities going on around them.

In addition to patients, the population includes doctors, nurses, technicians, other staff, and a steady stream of visitors and outside vendors and contractors. This group likely includes a variety of individuals that may have their own set of vulnerabilities. However, because their duties take them throughout the facility, they're almost as difficult to isolate from the impacts of cleaning as the patients. The typical hospital is busy 24 hours a day, 7 days a week.

Prioritizing cleaning activities

Most cleaning operations in health care (and other facilities as well) tend to treat all areas the same way. This practice leads to overcleaning many areas and, as budgets are cut, undercleaning more critical areas in an attempt to keep things in balance. By ranking each area in terms of the potential risk to patients and devising a cleaning plan to meet the need, you can ensure that scarce labor dollars are spent as effectively as possible.

In the typical hospital, about 45 to 65 percent of the facility may be classified as noncritical or low risk. Medium-risk areas comprise about 25 to 45 percent of the facility, and only about 10 percent are critical or high-risk areas. An important step in your plan is to classify every area in the hospital according to its risk level. The following is one example of how these areas might be classified:

✔ Noncritical areas are cleaned much the same way as a typical office facility and might include

- Exterior

- Administration, accounting, records, HR, and so on

- Patient registration and waiting areas

- Shops, printing, mail room, materials management

- Hallways

✔ Semicritical areas require more frequent, detailed attention and are those such as:

- Public restrooms

- Nursery

- Clinics, outpatients, diabetes, respiratory therapy

- Rehabilitation, physical therapy, cardiac rehabilitation

✔ Critical areas require the most attention and include:

- Emergency room

- Labor and delivery areas

- Morgue

- Surgery

Patient rooms can fall into any of the three risk areas, depending on the patient. For example, a patient being treated for addiction may be considered noncritical, and a patient in the burn unit would be part of the critical category.

Ranking the areas in a hospital depends on a lot of factors and therefore comes with no single right answer. Your green team (see Chapter 4) looks at all the characteristics of the hospital, its employees and patients, and the cleaning capabilities of the janitorial staff to prioritize cleaning tasks.

Work with the hospital's Infection Control Committee to develop a green cleaning plan, and set staffing levels and cleaning intensity to match the relative risk levels of each area.

Focusing the highest level of intensity only in the critical areas frees up valuable labor and product resources, allowing more effective cleaning without adding staff.

Fighting illness

Although improving the overall environmental quality of the facility and thereby protecting the health of the population is the key goal, health care facilities need to consider another goal as well: breaking the chain of infection and reducing nosocomial infections.

Nosocomial infections are hospital-acquired illnesses — a patient being treated for one illness or injury succumbs to another infection while in the hospital. Every year more than 2 million patients — almost 6 percent of all patients — acquire these infections in the United States. Seventy thousand, or almost 4 percent of these infections are fatal. Approximately one-third are preventable.

This is *not* an indictment of the cleaning industry, nor are we suggesting that all or even the majority of nosocomial infections can be laid at the feet of the cleaning operations. However, focusing cleaning attention where it's most critically needed — such as on those things that people touch and can transfer contamination from one person to another — combined with an improved hand-washing program can improve these statistics.

Building the green team

Your green team should include the infection control department, nursing staff, and representatives of other key stakeholder groups. Although it may be impractical to include actual patient representatives on your green team, most health care facilities have a *patient ombudsman.* This individual is generally charged with representing patient interests with the hospital staff, and his participation on your team is important. For more info on building a green team, see Chapter 4.

Advocacy groups in this industry actively work to improve the environment within hospitals. One of the leading organizations is Hospitals for a Healthy Environment. You can find contact information for this and other advocacy groups in the appendixes.

Facing unique challenges

Four major challenges face you as you implement a green cleaning program in health care:

✔ **Scheduling issues:** Hospitals are active day and night; some areas, such as emergency rooms, literally never shut down. Working around doctors, nurses, other staff, and patients can be very challenging. This consideration should guide your choices in cleaning chemicals (odor, caustic levels, toxicity) equipment (noise levels, size, and maneuverability) and procedures (amount of water used, timing, sprays versus wipes, and so on).

Schedule major work such as carpet cleaning and stripping and recoating floors when they'll have the lowest possible impact.

You're going to have to be flexible to allow for emergencies and other issues, and remember to share your schedules with the groups and areas they impact.

✔ **Changing cleaning intensities to match risk areas:** The cornerstone to an effective green cleaning program in these facilities is reclassifying the various areas according to potential risk levels, and matching cleaning intensities to each level. Your challenge is to build a solid case for how you have divided the facility and explain that your proposal isn't a *reduction* in cleaning as much as it is *raising* the intensity in the appropriate areas. In spite of what anyone wants to believe, chances are very slim that the entire facility is being cleaned at a high-risk level of intensity today.

✔ **Dealing with the Infection Control Committee and getting buy-in to change approved processes:** Change is hard in any situation, and it's particularly difficult in a health care facility because of the regulations it must meet and accreditation process that it goes through. Keeping these from being a barrier to change takes real knowledge and skill, and ultimately the support of your green team.

> ✔ **Being treated as a professional:** You're dealing with very well-educated professionals. These people may well look at someone from the cleaning staff as less qualified to speak about many of these issues. The only way to be treated as a professional is to be professional. That's much more than using $25 words and dressing well. It means doing your homework, learning about the issues involved in protecting human health, and about the impacts of chemicals and cleaning activities on patients and staff. Become as educated in your field as your colleagues in the health care industry are in theirs.

Becoming a Green Cleaning Contractor

The majority of office buildings in the United States are cleaned by BSCs (building service contractors) as opposed to having their own employees do the cleaning. Although BSCs haven't penetrated the education and health care markets to the same degree, they're a significant presence and growing. If your organization is a cleaning contractor, this section is for you.

Contractors face a few concerns that arise from their status:

> ✔ Does going green mean that all cleaning operations performed by your company will be green, regardless of the customer's wishes?
>
> ✔ What happens if the client specifies the product to be used and it isn't green?
>
> ✔ What if the cleaning specifications provided by the client (and required by the contract) don't meet your green standards?

In this section, we focus on some of the unique characteristics of this type of company.

Trying to take your company in a certain direction — moving toward green cleaning — while respecting and servicing the needs of dozens or hundreds of unique clients can be daunting. The rewards — distinguishing yourself from the competition, establishing a leadership position in your industry, protecting the health and well-being of your employees as well as hundreds or thousands of occupants of your clients' buildings, and making a difference in the overall environment — are pretty significant as well.

Planning, and then planning some more

The green cleaning plan you build for your business isn't the only one you need as a contractor. You create a multitude of green cleaning plans — one for each facility.

Relax; you're not reinventing the wheel each time. Most of each building plan comes right out of your company green cleaning program. You modify that basic plan to meet the needs of a specific facility's population, use, and other unique characteristics. You usually work with the facility's green team to develop these plans, so the actual amount of additional work for your staff is somewhat limited.

Setting green cleaning goals

Your organization is concerned with two types of green cleaning goals: those established for and by your company and those of your various clients.

Although your company executes or even leads a significant part of your client's green cleaning program, you are part of *their* green team and working toward *their* green cleaning goals.

Some clients specify the products, equipment, and paper that you use in their facility, which puts you in a difficult spot when those products don't live up to your green standards. In order to continue offering your clients and employees a better way of cleaning (and to stay in business), take the following actions:

- ✔ Explain to your client or prospect the advantages of using green products. Given the advances in technology and the competitive marketplace, green products are as effective as (or more effective than) traditional products, and they cost about the same. Making some relatively small changes creates a better workplace without increasing costs.

- ✔ Ensure your employees follow all manufacturers' use and safety instructions for any chemicals used. Issue and require the use of appropriate personal protective equipment. Premix all concentrates and issue only properly labeled RTU containers to the cleaning staff. Modify cleaning procedures to minimize potential exposure to employees and other building occupants.

Green cleaning is a journey, and you don't have to make all the changes at one time. Our best advice is to make sound business decisions while moving in the right direction. After all, you won't be helping your clients, employees, or the environment if you don't stay in business.

Building a team within a team

Your organization's green team will be a part of the green teams in your clients' organizations as they implement green cleaning programs.

The actual makeup of your internal green team depends in large part on the size and complexity of your organization. Many building service contractors run extremely lean operations. Managers and company officers often wear several hats. Choosing your team leader is very critical in this situation. The team leader should be emotionally invested in the program's success and committed to seeing it through. This may mean choosing an individual who has demonstrated this sort of enthusiasm and commitment but doesn't have significant "position power."

Don't set the team leader up to fail. Make it clear to your appointed leader as well as the rest of the organization that he *is* the team leader. What this person lacks in position power must be granted in influence by you as the head of the company. Then back your words with action. Give your team leader some room to make mistakes and back him up when he really needs it.

Chapter 4

Getting Everyone on Board

●●●

●●●

*N*o green cleaning program can come to fruition without the support of several critical players, from your cleaning and maintenance personnel, who implement the changes in their day-to-day activities, to the building management and occupants whose approval, support, and cooperation you need. Before you can make your good intentions reality, you have some convincing to do. In this chapter, we show you how to put together the information that makes the sale and how to construct the team that gets things moving.

Although we label this the agreement stage, you need to go beyond simply getting management to agree to the need for a green cleaning program. After you get the initial agreement, you need to help build some teams to get your project moving, measure the baseline (current situation), and develop the implementation plan. Only then are you in a position to return to management to lay out the entire program and build the consensus to see it through to success.

Getting Agreement to Move Forward

Getting to an agreement involves two key issues:

✔ Making sure the key stakeholders (usually upper management or the administration) agree they want a green cleaning program.

✔ Getting agreement as to what a green cleaning program is. Simply put, we're talking about expectation management.

So, how do you go from, "Hey, these guys make green cleaning sound really great" to getting management approval for development of a green cleaning program? If you're in sales, you'll see right away that selling green cleaning to the boss is just like selling any intangible. And, if you're not in sales don't worry, we'll walk you through the steps right now.

Key to selling any *intangible,* something you can't see, touch, smell or hear, is to make it tangible to your prospect. Help them feel, see, smell, and hear it. The amount of detail, method of presentation, and key points of focus will vary depending on the nature of your organization. However, there are three basic steps involved:

1. **Help management understand what's in it for them.** People want to buy solutions to their problems. As you construct your presentation, remember to focus your *value proposition,* the reason someone should buy your plan, on management's needs. Help them "touch" your ideas, "see" how they solve their problems, and "feel" the peace of mind that will come from agreeing to your proposition. Take the following steps:

   • Define green and green cleaning.

   • Explain the potential health and performance benefits.

   • Explain the opportunity for improving occupant satisfaction and reducing complaints.

   • Discuss the marketing benefits where applicable.

   • Highlight risk reduction.

2. **Let them see what's involved; explain the process.** Walk them through the steps:

   • Audits of housekeeping, chemicals, equipment, paper, mats, supplies, and so on to build the baseline.

   • Plan development, which can identify the easy and inexpensive steps, the difficult and costly, and the rest in between.

   • Plan presentation, remind them that this minimizes their risk as they have the ultimate option to request modifications or simply say no.

3. **Ask for the order.** You sales pros know what we mean. For the rest of you, this means after you've presented your arguments to management, ask them to agree to move forward.

   If they aren't quite ready to commit yet, that's okay. Change is difficult, and remember, they haven't had a chance to read this book yet. Ask for agreement to conduct the building audits and rework your value proposition. When you go back for the next presentation you'll know at least two things you didn't know the first time:

- You'll have much more data about the *actual* condition of the building after conducting the audits.

- You'll know management's hot buttons. Those were the items they asked the most questions about the first time. Now you're ready for them and have the answers before the questions are even asked.

It ain't easy going green

Reaching agreement among the various stakeholders and teams is the most important and difficult of all the stages. Without clear agreement on direction and mandate, your team is likely to flounder during the planning stage. Be patient and persistent and keep in mind that what you're attempting comes with a full set of difficulties that you need to address and overcome:

- ✔ You're proposing change. By nature, people are resistant to change. Change is perceived as hard, time consuming, and threatening.

- ✔ You're working with very busy people. They likely have full days already and are reluctant to take on more responsibility. In fact, the best people, the ones you really want, are probably the busiest *because* they're the best. You have to present your case well to engage them.

- ✔ You're bringing together a variety of departments and groups with competing agendas. You need to be sensitive to potential turf wars and interdepartmental conflicts and jealousies.

- ✔ Bias about cleaning is rampant. The higher up in an organization you go, the lower a priority cleaning seems to be, especially if no one is complaining about it. Thus, you need to convince upper management that your plan is worth their time and is a worthwhile endeavor for their organization.

Unfortunately, we can't give you a magic formula to suddenly make everyone get along. The most important thing you can do is to prepare your introduction carefully and thoroughly. As you build your case for implementing a green cleaning program, stress the impacts of cleaning on each and every group you address. Bring the points down to a personal level to help each person feel and understand the importance and need for this program.

For some, health issues may be the critical issue. For others, it may be environmental benefits. And for others it may be financial, cost avoidance, productivity, marketing, community relations, sustainability, meeting organizational, legislative, or regulatory requirements, and other issues. Do your research on potential recruits. Look for people who already get the idea of green and for influencers who can help you move the organization.

Cleaning, or more specifically, judging the "quality" of cleaning has traditionally tended to be a subjective exercise. As you begin to introduce the concept of green cleaning, a whole new level of subjective expectations arises. A key goal at this stage is to develop the data to support your plan in order to get everyone on board with your proposed green cleaning program.

The success of the later stages (for instance, stewardship) depends explicitly on the understanding and agreement of all participants.

Building the Green Teams

To carry forward your green cleaning program, we recommend you establish two teams:

- A *steering committee* comprised of senior management as well as other key stakeholders, such as labor union representatives, tenant or department representatives, and operations management.

 The steering committee is responsible for maintaining the project's momentum, which becomes especially important in the face of inevitable internal and external political hurdles that result from making significant changes and competition for scarce resources. The steering committee must provide the clout to navigate these often difficult waters. They also need to ensure that the green team stays on track and has the resources necessary to succeed.

- An *action team,* which we call the *green team,* that includes the people who are responsible for the day-to-day activities and details involved in implementing the plan, from collecting the initial information (baseline) that reviews the current situation to reviewing results and modifying procedures to achieve the desired results. (We talk more about this group in Chapter 8.)

Note: Different types of facilities have different stakeholders and require different types of team members. In the upcoming sections, we provide examples from several types of facilities.

There is no one correct way to set up these teams. In some cases, a single team may be capable of addressing both missions, while in others, separate teams and charters may be required. In cases where you employ separate teams, communication between the steering committee and the green team is critical to avoid conflict, confusion, and duplication of efforts.

Naming a coordinator

As you begin to help build the steering committee and green team, keep in mind that you want to appoint one person as the leader or coordinator. This person works with both the steering committee and the green team.

Selecting the right coordinator is as important as choosing the rest of the team. Even with your best intentions, a green cleaning program doesn't just happen. It takes planning, teamwork, and communication to create and sustain an effective program. The coordinator can be a person from any of the groups represented in your teams. An ability to communicate, manage multiple priorities and processes, and foster a sense of teamwork is the critical trait for this position.

The primary role of the coordinator is team management and leadership. Specific functions include:

✔ **Leadership:** Coordinating the green cleaning steering committee and green team.

✔ **Communication:** Ensuring the steering committee and green team have the information needed to make timely and informed decisions, that stakeholders are kept apprised of progress, and answering questions in a timely and accurate fashion.

✔ **Problem-solving:** Being aware of any problems that may be developing, coordinating efforts to deal with them quickly, and calling for outside assistance when appropriate.

✔ **Point of contact:** Serving as point person for all questions, communications, concerns, or other issues between the implementation teams, management, administration, staff, tenants, employees, and the press.

A number of factors influence your choice for coordinator, including the size or structure of the facility. Your decision should be guided by the level of authority required for the project as well as the individual's genuine interest in leading this effort. In some cases, an outside individual such as a vendor, consultant, or green cleaning advocate can serve as the coordinator, but frequently these people play the role of key advisor to the coordinator.

The coordinator doesn't need to be an expert in cleaning or environmental issues. By using resources such as this book and the materials referenced in this book, the coordinator, as well as the rest of the team, discovers key issues to implement the green cleaning program.

Choosing the green team

One of the keys to successfully implementing a green cleaning program in a facility is to choose and empower an effective *green team*. These are the people who are going to make your plan happen on a day-to-day basis, so you want to make sure that you build an effective team.

Although the membership of the steering committee is relatively small and straightforward (as mentioned earlier, this is the senior management group who will help remove obstacles for the green team) choosing the members of the green team can be a bit more complicated.

Here are a few tips for creating a team that moves your program forward:

- ✔ Include members from *all* stakeholder groups in the facility. The quickest way to create a roadblock is to exclude a group and suffer the resentment that can result. In the section, "Special Considerations for Team Building," we discuss some of the possible stakeholders in various types of facilities.

- ✔ If certain occupants in the facility have expressed an interest or concern about improving the quality of the indoor environment, consider asking them to join the group. When things get tough, it helps to have members that are self-motivated and dedicated to solutions.

- ✔ Every organization has the "old-timer" who remembers when things were done this way or that way and knows all the reasons the new ways won't work. Make friends with this individual; let him discover the advantages of the program and you'll have an evangelist. If you don't know this person at the facility, ask around, and someone will point him out.

- ✔ Look outside of the organization's employees. Include vendors, service providers, visitors, customers, and others. In essence, you want to include everyone who uses, visits, impacts, or is impacted by the facility.

- ✔ Consider including representatives from cleaning supply vendors. These individuals can be an excellent source of information, and they have access to training programs as well as more detailed information about the products, equipment, and supplies from the manufacturers. You may find vendors in your area that have already participated in this type of activity and can help you move more efficiently.

Special Considerations for Team Building

We can't detail the makeup of a green team for every possible type of organization or facility. However, we can provide some direction for a few key building types. We hope that looking over our recommendations for these types of organizations helps you come up with your own list quite easily, even if we don't cover your particular situation.

Building teams in schools

Although this list is geared primarily at kindergarten through high school, you could use this as a starting point for building a team in a university setting. If you work in a school, consider the following individuals as members of your green team:

- ✔ **Administration (often the principal):** Their decisions make quite an impact on the indoor environment of the school, and they have the standing to ensure the plans are carried out.

- ✔ **Plant operations:** This group has direct control over the heating, cooling, ventilation, and other environmental controls of the facility. They're also responsible for choosing and using products such as paint, flooring, adhesives, and other construction materials. The plan must be congruent with their mission to keep the school in good repair, or conflict can derail your efforts.

- ✔ **Custodians:** Typically represented by the head custodian on the team, custodians are of course responsible for the daily maintenance of the school. They're also usually responsible for setting up and cleaning up after special activities. In many schools, the custodian is also responsible for overseeing non-school activities in the building. Too often overlooked when planning changes, these people are a key to your success.

- ✔ **Teachers:** Incredibly important stakeholders, teachers can have a direct impact on the level of pollutants in their rooms by controlling ventilation as well as by choosing the materials they bring into and use in the room. A science teacher may be able to translate what you share with her about green cleaning into a curriculum for her students.

- ✔ **School nurse:** No one can better help you understand the baseline levels of reported illnesses and health issues in the school. Nurses can help monitor changes and improvements as the plan is implemented.

✔ **School board representatives:** These folks control the purse strings. Rather than risk battles over budget questions, get ahead of the game by involving them and making a representative a member of the team.

✔ **Contract service providers:** Often forgotten, this group includes bus and transportation services, cleaning contractors, elevator maintenance companies, roofing or painting contractors, HVAC technicians, and so on. Look around the school and you may be surprised at how many service providers work in the school. Their activities can have dramatic impacts on the types and amounts of pollutants introduced into the building.

✔ **Students:** The main occupants of your building, students not only need to be aware of what's happening in their school, they need to understand how their actions have an impact on the health of the entire building. Making them a part of the process helps you gain cooperation and understanding. This is especially valuable if dealing with graffiti and vandalism.

✔ **Parents:** The importance of communicating with parents may be clear, but don't forget to solicit their involvement and participation, as well. Many have talents, skills, and interests that are useful in the planning and implementation process. Plus, they can influence the school board and budgets.

Creating teams in office buildings

An office may mean a few employees in a small building or tens of thousands of employees spread throughout several campuses. The team may just be you and your assistant or a group of several dozen from various departments. In this section, we consider a multi-tenant building managed by a professional management company. You can add or delete members and groups to fit your unique needs.

Engaging building occupants is important in any office building, but even more so in a multi-tenant building. Much of what you do to green a building isn't readily apparent to the occupants. Certainly, you reduce environmental impacts, and hopefully over time occupants feel better as a result of your actions; however, as you take these actions, the effect isn't obvious. Keeping occupants informed and engaged in the process helps draw attention to the positive steps you're taking and prevents the inevitable doubts and questions from getting in the way of your efforts.

Key participants should be drawn from the following groups:

✔ Property management

✔ Tenant representatives

✔ Building operations

✔ In-house custodians or contract cleaning company

✔ Health, safety, or environmental officer

✔ Risk management

✔ Other service providers, such as HVAC, elevator, roofing, trash removal and recycling, indoor plants, landscaping, lighting, construction, vending, pest management, and so on

Your facility may not have all of these groups or may have additional groups that should be represented. The point is to be certain that you have included representatives from all of the stakeholders in the facility.

We have found that every business has two organizations — the formal organization of managers and employees reflected by the organizational chart, and the informal organization or "gossip mill." Don't underestimate the influence and power of this informal organization. You will do well to tap into this group. It can generate tremendous support and resources to your plan. This group also has a communication network that's likely faster and more efficient than any formal communication system you can envision. The best way to tap into this group is to look for one of the more vocal members and recruit them to join your team.

Considering teams in health care settings

Whether you work in a clinic, long-term care facility, or hospital, certain groups need to be represented on the green team. The size and complexity of the facility dictates the actual members, but the critical point is to include representatives from every stakeholder group. Some of the folks to consider are:

✔ Administration and staff

✔ Nurses

✔ Doctors

✔ Other professional staff

✔ Infection control

✔ Purchasing

✔ Housekeeping

✔ Building operations

✓ Patient advocates

✓ Contract service providers

✓ Laundry

✓ Food services

✓ Transportation

✓ Community relations

Part II
Going Green

"A large part of our success is based on our ability to implement a safe, healthy cleaning program and of course, avoid conflicts."

In this part . . .

*I*mplementing a green cleaning program is a process in which you seek better ways to create healthier environments. It is a process itself, one divided into three stages with specific actions, mileposts, and goals. Successful completion of each stage is critical to the success of the next. We developed this approach to make the entire process easier to understand and measure. The three stages of implementation are agreement, implementation, and stewardship.

In the next several chapters, we tell you about each stage in detail.

Chapter 5

Establishing the Baseline and Building the Plan

In This Chapter

▶ Summing up a building's starting point

▶ Addressing what's right and what needs work

▶ Drumming up enthusiasm for your plan

*U*ntil you know where you stand, you can't see the path to your green cleaning goals. You and your team therefore need to establish your baseline — that is, you need to take a look at the current situation in the building. After you get a grip on the opportunities and challenges that exist in the building, you can begin outlining your plan for improvement. In this chapter, we show you how to determine your building's status and prepare for its progress.

Identifying the State of Things

To fully grasp the current state of a building, your green team should conduct a number of facility and housekeeping surveys. Consider the following points as you plan the surveys:

✔ **Pick items that you can realistically measure.** It might sound nice to say we are going to capture air quality readings; the reality is that doing so is very difficult and expensive. Effective metering devices cost several thousand dollars, and a host of variables affects the readings. Don't bite off too much.

✔ **Be sensitive to privacy concerns.** Although capturing aggregate performance data, absenteeism, missed school days, or nurse visits might be fine, accessing specific personnel records is likely to be a problem.

✔ **Capture data that is actionable.** Collecting data for data's sake wastes the team's valuable time. Focus on key measures that you can address in the plan and communicate.

The following are some typical survey items. You don't have to do all of them, but it's important that everyone agrees what will be done and that the surveys are thorough.

✔ **Perform an existing cleaning chemical inventory.** At a minimum, record each product and its manufacturer's name, along with where in the building the product is located. Other valuable information includes how the product is used and which containers are old, damaged, or leaking. And make sure you capture all products including obsolete inventory, single containers, and products designated for disposal to insure the inventory is accurate and to be able to take credit for eliminating these products.

Although you need to be sure you visit every janitorial closet and supply area, don't limit your search. Walk through the building and look on desks, in closets, breakroom cupboards, nooks, and crannies for cleaning supplies, including those that may have been brought from home. Make special note of these items and check to see whether all items are properly labeled.

After you complete the cleaning chemical inventory, compare your list with the material safety data sheets (MSDS) to make sure one is available for each product.

✔ **Perform an existing cleaning equipment inventory.** While capturing the actual count, be sure to check each machine to see whether it works, note its general condition, looking for broken plugs, frayed cords, missing parts, and so on. You may also want to capture equipment serial numbers and note any repair logs.

✔ **Evaluate janitorial paper and trash can liners.** Make note of recycled content and be sure your paper products actually fit the dispensers in your building. (You'd be surprised at how many cases of paper in a building don't fit any dispensers!) Check trash can liners, as well. Too often, large bags are used in small containers or small bags are stretched to fit larger containers.

✔ **Evaluate and record any other janitorial tools and supplies.** Be on the lookout for dust mops, wet mops, handles, frames, buckets, cloth wipers (rags), spray bottles, dispensers, feather or wool dusters, microfiber cloths, and so on. Make note of the condition of these products, how they're stored, and whether they're appropriate for the areas they're being used in.

✔ **Conduct an analysis of the janitorial closets and storage areas.** Note their general cleanliness, organization, space, lighting, water supply and sink, ventilation, shelving, and so on. You may be very surprised at how difficult it is to work in and from these closets!

✔ **Conduct a general housekeeping walkthrough.** Evaluate the overall quality of the current cleaning and look for problems as well as opportunities for improvement.

As you walk through the facility, start on the outside and look at how soils are being brought into the building. Inside the building, check for clues that the occupants aren't satisfied with the level of cleaning or general comfort in the building. Some of these clues include cleaning products brought from home, personal air filters, and personal space heaters. Other clues are pieces of cardboard taped to air diffusers (to direct the air away from or toward an area), rags, or microfiber cloths on desks.

✔ **Go over your cleaning log.** If your organization uses a log to communicate with the cleaning staff, read through it and create a simple spreadsheet of comments, complaints, requests, and compliments.

✔ **Document any recycling programs in place.** In your walk-through, pay attention to recycling containers. Are they being used properly?

✔ **Get a copy of the current cleaning specifications.** Make another spreadsheet that breaks out the tasks by frequency. Review this sheet with your cleaning manager. Are the specifications being followed? Where they are not, make notes regarding why the specifications aren't being followed. In some cases it may be that management has changed the specs, but the document was never updated.

✔ **Read the training manual.** If the cleaning staff has an operations or training manual that describes the various tasks they perform and how to perform them properly, get a copy for your records and planning process.

✔ **Examine data.** In schools, you might want to record nurse visits and missed school days (due to illness) for the previous year.

✔ **Do a survey.** Because cleaning is subjective, consider conducting a general housekeeping satisfaction survey of the building occupants. In many facilities key people in each area are appointed to collect comments and complaints for review with the housekeeping staff. Surveying these points of contact can be a way of keeping your task more manageable.

A word of caution about subjective satisfaction surveys: Occupants of a building usually have no awareness of exactly what the cleaning specifications are. A contract cleaning company may be directed to remove dry trash three times per week, but if the occupants don't know this, they're likely dismayed to find trash isn't emptied two times per week. An issue like this colors occupants' perception of the overall cleaning. When you see negative responses in a survey, probe a bit for specific examples of problems.

Developing Your Green Cleaning Plan

The green team should develop a green cleaning plan based on all the information that they collected and then prioritized in order to make sure that everyone is on the same page. The plan typically covers what products and procedures will be changed, including when those changes will happen, and who will be responsible.

Even in a relatively simple building, you need to collect a great deal of information before you can assess the building's baseline. The next step is to analyze the information the team has collected and look for the best opportunities for improvement.

As you analyze the results of the baseline surveys, prioritize the opportunities. Keep in mind the definition of green cleaning: "reducing the impacts on health and the environment compared to similar products and services." You need to look for and document the changes you propose for products, procedures, and other pollution-prevention strategies.

One proven approach is to create three categories of opportunities according to affordability and ease. You have a category for projects that are easy to implement and low- or no-cost, one for those on the other end of the spectrum, and one for middle-of-the road projects.

There is no right or wrong plan. The key is to develop a plan that gets buy-in from your team, upper management, and the steering committee. The initial plan must be developed so that you can show results after you implement each stage.

You don't have to do everything at once, so don't get bogged down at this stage. By getting the plan in place, achieving real results, and communicating progress, you provide the springboard for the more-challenging opportunities and continual improvement.

The specific points in your plan depend on the findings from your baseline survey. Successful plans often address:

✔ Cleaning chemicals (Chapter 10)

- Replace all noncertified cleaning chemicals with products that meet Green Seal, Environmental Choice, or other certification standards.

- Replace all RTU (ready to use) and bulk products with locked dispensing, proportioning systems, and premeasured pouches.

- Remove all disinfectants and sanitizers except in areas that specifically require their use.

✔ Waste (Chapter 6)

- Implement a recycling program.

- Standardize waste receptacle sizes and purchase liners appropriate for the sizes.

✔ Floor care (Chapters 10 and 13)

- Implement a sustainable floor-care program.

- Replace traditional dust mops, damp mops, and finish application mops with microfiber flat mops to capture more dust and improve productivity and ergonomics. Replace feather or wool dusters and all cloth wipers with microfiber cloths to improve productivity and performance.

- Install an effective matting system to reduce introduction of outdoor pollutants.

✔ Janitorial paper products (Chapter 12)

- Replace current janitorial paper products made from virgin tree fiber with products made from recycled products, tree-free fibers, or rapidly renewable resources.

- Replace multifold hand towels with large roll towels, and use hands-free dispensers.

✔ Equipment (Chapter 11)

- Replace current vacuum cleaners with ergonomically designed units that better retain microscopic dust particles and other potential irritants.

- Ensure that each piece of equipment is in usable condition and meets all safety guidelines. Prioritize potential for replacement based on each piece's ability to meet green recommendations and improved ergonomics.

✔ Procedures (Chapter 6)

- Modify cleaning procedures to accomplish tasks that require the use of potentially irritating chemicals or involve wet floors or carpets during times when fewer occupants are in the building and allow sufficient time for floors to properly dry and any odors to be dissipated.

- Clean and organize all janitorial closets and supply areas. Ensure all water supplies and drains function properly. Install adequate lighting and evaluate options to improve ventilation.

- Provide hand sanitizers in "high touch" areas of the facility such as reception areas and near elevators and public telephones.

- Establish a policy against eating at desks to help prevent pest infestations.

✔ Implement a green cleaning training program (Chapter 7)

Many other options may come to light in your particular analysis. Some might be much more ambitious, such as installing hands-free devices in your restrooms, buying a new carpet extractor, and so on. Again, the key is to look initially for those items that can make a significant impact and that you can implement relatively easily. As the team gains experience and credibility with established successes, you can set your sights higher.

Getting Everyone on Board

After your team has collected the baseline data, conducted their analysis, and prioritized their actions, the time is right for meeting again with the steering committee. At this meeting, your team lays out their findings and their plan, seeking the buy-in from the steering committee.

After you figure out what you want to do, you may be tempted to just get to it. However, getting the steering committee's support and participation in the stewardship process is critical. The group is responsible for getting the resources you need and helping to remove the stumbling blocks that you may encounter during implementation.

The steering committee is responsible for managing expectations, and one important aspect of that task is driving home to people who use the building that no program is going to make a building perfect. We can't ensure that no one, no matter how sensitive they are, will never have a symptom related to using a certain product or procedure.

Your goal is not perfection, but rather to make things *better*. You're seeking to reduce health and environmental impacts compared to the previous system.

Chapter 6

Green Cleaning Procedures

The techniques of green cleaning aren't significantly different from those employed in traditional cleaning systems. The differences aren't so much in the *how-to's* as in the *whys*.

Traditional cleaning systems tend to focus on the appearance of clean. The procedures used are focused on meeting the subjective standard as quickly and cost effectively as possible with minimal concern for impacts on the people involved or on the environment.

Green cleaning focuses on the following two *whys:*

✔ **Reducing potential negative exposures to both human health and the environment:** The focus is on procedures that help reduce these impacts. (Acceptable appearance levels follow.)

✔ **Identifying efficiencies:** This results in a cleaner building along with the ability to reallocate labor for other cleaning activities.

Building occupants expect to see something different when you implement a green cleaning program. To head off dissatisfaction, you need to set and manage expectations. We show you in Chapter 9 how to point out the differences in the new program versus the old system along with the advantages.

The concept of green cleaning — reducing health and environmental impacts — can be applied to any systemized cleaning process such as team cleaning, day cleaning, zone cleaning, and so on. The key point is that cleaning is a process, and green cleaning is more than just switching a few chemicals or using recycled products but must result in effective cleaning.

Furthermore, as we show you in Chapter 1, green cleaning is concerned about product and labor efficiency, but it's cost neutral: The cost of green cleaning is comparable to that of traditional cleaning if the building is currently using an effective cleaning system. However, if you discover during the baseline audit (see Chapter 5) that additional cleaning is required to create a healthier and more productive environment, this may in fact result in an increase in costs. But these costs are because of better cleaning rather than green cleaning.

Meeting Green Cleaning Goals

A green cleaning program reduces exposures of building occupants, visitors, and custodians to cleaning chemicals that may make it into the air they breathe, be absorbed through the skin, or even be accidentally ingested.

That's the human element of reducing exposures, but there's also an environmental element. To protect the health of the environment, you're looking for procedures that:

- ✔ Use fewer types of chemicals. Every new chemical you add to the janitor closet represents additional resource consumption, packaging material, transportation impacts, and disposal impacts on the environment. Simpler is better.

- ✔ Reduce the amount of chemicals, paper, trash can liners, and other consumable products that you use.

- ✔ Use green-certified chemicals, paper, equipment, and other supplies.

- ✔ Waste less by using more concentrated products or procedures that are more resource efficient.

- ✔ Extend the life of durable equipment, tools, and other supplies.

Another potential benefit to this exercise is that by using fewer chemicals and smaller quantities, you may find savings in purchasing and inventory costs.

Green cleaning is *not* an exercise in labor or cost reduction. However, wasting labor and spending more time and effort to clean than is necessary takes away time and resources that could be used to improve cleaning in other areas of the building. Thus, you want to look for equipment that performs more effectively and efficiently. (Generally this equipment will last longer and show a much higher return on investment than that which it replaced.)

Looking for efficiencies also means looking at what you clean and adjusting intensities to make the overall operation more efficient. For example, by spending more time and effort in cleaning entryways, you can stop a significant portion of pollutants from entering the building. Doing so helps reduce the frequencies required for general dusting and floor-care programs. Improving an entryway matting system can assist in this effort as well. (See Chapter 13.)

Along the same lines, using burnishing equipment that has active vacuum attachments and vacuum cleaners with better filtration systems cuts down the amount of dust recirculated through the building and can reduce the required frequency of dusting.

Finally, the *order* in which the procedures are performed can have a significant impact on labor efficiency. A simple reminder helps: start high and dry. For example, start with high dusting and move down, vacuuming last. This gets gravity working for you as a free employee! As you clean, the dust will naturally tend to fall to lower surfaces; by starting at the top you avoid cleaning the same area twice. The same sort of thinking can be applied to other procedures in your workflow. Look for ways to avoid repeating steps or routes as you move through the building.

Take a look at the following procedure changes to determine how you can make your program greener:

- *How* a procedure is performed
- *When* it is performed
- The *products or equipment* used to perform the procedure
- The *sequence* in which procedures are performed

Minimizing change is an important consideration when you're changing procedures. Huh? After listing all the possible changes and opportunities, we tell you to minimize change? The point is to be smart about making changes. Change is difficult, and you need to manage the whole process. Make it easier for the plan to succeed by:

- Beginning with the most important procedures — those that can reduce direct risks to the workers' or building occupants' health.
- Developing a process for continual improvement. Chapter 8 shows you how.

Digging In to Common Procedure Changes

We don't mean for this list to be exhaustive; it simply represents some of the most commonly identified opportunities for making changes in many facilities. This book doesn't take the place of a procedure manual.

We highlight key opportunities and how they differ from traditional methods. We assume you already know how to accomplish basic cleaning procedures. (And if you don't, check out some of the excellent procedure manuals available from the ISSA Bookstore, which you can find at www.issa.com.) Okay, ready to get your hands dirty?

Identify vulnerable populations

A significant difference between a green cleaning program and traditional programs is the consideration paid to *vulnerable populations* — those people who for various reasons are more sensitive to environmental conditions or the effects of cleaning. (We talk about vulnerable populations in detail in Chapters 1 and 2.) Traditionally, we schedule our cleaning operations to move through a building in a logical sequence, maximizing efficiencies for the cleaning staff, which may not be the best process for addressing the needs of vulnerable populations.

A green cleaning program addresses this situation by:

- Identifying the occupants with special needs or sensitivities
- Making changes in the products used in these areas to minimize exposures to irritating materials
- Making changes to cleaning schedules to minimize exposures to the cleaning products and processes

In some cases, you may need to address ventilation issues or relocate these people to other areas of the building to better serve their individual needs.

 The goal of a cleaning program is to reduce occupants' exposure to irritants and pollutants, but sometimes the act of cleaning actually increases their discomfort levels. In many cases, changing the cleaning schedule can have a dramatic positive impact. Schedule cleaning operations for times when the sensitive occupants are away from their workspaces, and be sure to allow sufficient time after cleaning for residues and fragrances to disperse. Changing the cleaning products to include those with minimal or no fragrances usually has a positive impact as well.

Focus on entryways

Increasing the effectiveness of the matting system and entryway cleaning captures and eliminates dirt and dust before it can penetrate deeper into the building. Effort here improves the indoor environmental quality while reducing the amount of labor required to remove dirt and dust throughout the building.

Here's how to keep dirt from getting in:

- ✔ **Vacuum first:** Effective vacuuming (with a good vacuum cleaner and collection system that retains the microscopic dust particles) removes many of the contaminants that affect health. Traditionally, entryways are cleaned at the end of the shift, when the custodian is tired and the vacuum full; the results are often less than adequate. Starting in the entry has the additional benefit of ensuring occupants' first impression is positive when they enter the building in the morning.

- ✔ **Address the outside:** The outside of entrances is as important as the inside. Sweep, hose down, or power wash the area leading into the building as needed. Reducing the amount of dirt hanging around immediately outside the building keeps it outside. Keeping the dirt outside reduces labor inside the building and extends the life of entryway mats.

- ✔ **Remember all entryways:** Too often the focus is on the main entry and other less-used entry points are neglected. Don't forget the entry leading from the parking structure or underground garage: The oily soils from these areas damage the floor finish and carpets if you don't capture them before they can be tracked throughout the building.

Check out Chapter 13 for tips on selection and placement of effective mats.

Dust mopping

Traditional dust mopping procedures tend to move the dust from place to place rather than capturing and removing contaminants. Additionally, many of the dust mop treatments are oil-based and leave a film on the floor. That film can lead to slips and falls, and it attracts more dirt and dust, which in turn requires more frequent floor-care procedures. Even the water-based treatments cause problems if you don't apply them properly.

 Consider using microfiber dust mops instead of the traditional cotton or nylon loop mop head. Microfiber cloths are designed to attract and retain the dust particles, preventing them from being redeposited elsewhere or kicked into the air. These tools are very lightweight and easy to use, which helps reduce fatigue and injury for the custodians.

Another alternative to traditional dust mopping is vacuuming hard floors. Using lightweight, ergonomically designed backpack vacuums or large-area vacuums, the custodian can cover large areas very quickly with minimal fatigue. Choosing vacuums with high-efficiency filtration systems ensures that the dust is captured and not simply moved around the building.

Dusting and spot cleaning surfaces

Like the dust mop, traditional dusting tools such as the feather duster or wool duster tend to move dust from one location to another, retaining very little. Treated cloths or rags and spray polish suffer from the same problems as dust mop treatment. They often leave a film that attracts more dust and fingerprints, and feels greasy to the occupants. All of these tend to be expensive as well.

Consider microfiber cloths for dusting and spot cleaning most surfaces. A dry microfiber cloth designed for dusting can retain three to four times the dust particles captured by traditional tools. You can easily launder them hundreds of times before you need to replace them.

You can find microfiber cloths designed for removing tougher marks and spots with no water or chemicals. These can be very effective for spot cleaning entry or door glass, mirrors, elevator panels, and so on. For extremely stubborn marks, a little water or general purpose cleaner combined with the microfiber cloth usually does the trick.

For damp or wet cleaning in break areas, kitchens, and restrooms, a special microfiber cloth outperforms traditional rags or paper towels, and you can use it with few or no chemicals. Along with superior cleaning, all of these microfiber products offer the opportunity to reduce exposure to cleaning chemicals because they are so effective with minimal chemical use or none at all. And they come with an additional benefit — reduced chemical costs!

When you plan the cleaning schedule, always dust first, and then vacuum or mop. Start high and dry — work down to the floor. Any dust not captured by the dusting process has several more chances to be captured ultimately with the dust mop or vacuum rather than being left to settle later.

A sustainable floor care program

As we show you in Chapter 10, a sustainable floor care program is one that delivers the desired level of appearance and is slip resist-ant with minimal maintenance. The goal is to reduce or eliminate the need for:

- ✔ **Spray buffing or burnishing:** Both processes are labor- and equipment-intensive, generate additional dust or spray prod-uct into the air, and increase maintenance costs.

- ✔ **Deep scrubbing and recoating:** This is a labor- and chemical-intensive process that increases exposure to potential irritants and opportunities for slip-fall accidents.

- ✔ **Stripping and refinishing:** The most labor-intensive part of a floor-care program, stripping and refinishing often require potentially dangerous products (stripping solution). This is a high-cost operation that increases the opportunity for injury.

A sustainable floor care program begins with selecting a system that is appropriate for the level and type of traffic in the building that meets the appearance standards. See Chapter 13 for tips on choosing floor-care systems.

Without adequate daily maintenance, the best floor-care system can't succeed. The good news is that the labor required for an effective daily maintenance program is much less expensive and easier than deep scrubbing or stripping. Dry mopping, spot mop-ping, or vacuuming the floors at least once a day (entryways and other high-traffic areas may require more frequent dry mopping or spot mopping.) is the keystone to extending time between more intensive projects.

Combined with effective matting systems, a green floor-care system and daily maintenance program deliver a sustainable floor-care pro-gram. Positive benefits include reduction of chemical exposure to workers and occupants, as well as reduced impacts on the environ-ment. As with many of the procedure changes we discuss, such a floor-care system can actually reduce the total cleaning costs.

Chemical application methods

To minimize the amount of chemicals in the air, look at how the custodians apply the cleaning products they use. One of the biggest offenders is the ubiquitous aerosol spray can. The good news is CFCs, which are harmful in the environment, were banned a long time ago. The bad news is we now generally use hydrocarbon propellants such as propane and butane, which create their own environmental burdens, and the particles coming out of the aerosol are extremely fine and dispersed in a wide pattern.

Typically the custodian holds an aerosol can a foot from the surface to be cleaned and broadcasts a jet spray of millions of fine particles into the air. These particles are the perfect size to get past the body's defenses and make their way straight into the lungs.

We aren't suggesting that aerosols are bad; you find many excellent uses for this dispensing container for paints, adhesives, and other products. However, when you're indoors the trigger spray bottle is a better alternative for cleaning products. The properly labeled bottle is filled from a proportioning device or premeasured packet to ensure the proper concentration. Adjust the spray pattern to a coarse spray or — better yet — a stream, and apply the product directly into your cleaning cloth, *not* on the surface to be cleaned.

A microfiber cleaning system is an even better method for chemical application. Most cloths will be used dry or with water, but the few that require a chemical can be carried premoistened in a tray, bucket, or plastic bag, ready for use. This system reduces potential exposure tremendously and reduces overuse and waste of expensive cleaning chemicals.

Carpet care

Like hard floor care, green carpet-care programs use procedures that are the same as or similar to traditional procedures. However, a few important differences exist.

An investment of effort at a building's entry points reduces the amount of dirt tracked across carpets in the rest of the building.

As with the other procedures we've discussed, a green carpet-care program begins with choosing the appropriate chemicals. See Chapter 10 for specific recommendations.

Equipment choice is the next consideration. Carpet acts like a sink, capturing and holding a tremendous amount of soil before it becomes apparent. A typical commercial carpet can hold five to ten times its weight in dirt before it becomes noticeable. As you look at commercial carpets, consider why most of them are earth tones!

The average "throw-away" vacuum cleaner just doesn't have what it takes to pull soil from deep inside the carpet fibers. And the dust it does pick up tends to be pushed right through the bag and back into the air to fall elsewhere. Investing in well-designed and well-made vacuum cleaners pays off in more than extended equipment life: It has a direct impact on the health of the building's occupants and the life of the carpet itself.

Regardless of daily maintenance, at some point carpets require more intensive cleaning. Some general considerations include the following:

- ✔ When spot cleaning, apply chemicals in a coarse spray or stream to minimize the fine particles that may be released into the air. Use a spot-cleaning system that's compatible with and recommended by the supplier of the green carpet-cleaning chemicals.

- ✔ Notify building occupants of any major carpet cleaning to be done well in advance of the scheduled date. Make any applicable MSD sheets available to concerned occupants.

- ✔ When extracting carpets, schedule the activity when the building is closed or has minimal occupancy for extended times, such as over weekends, holidays, or other shut-down periods.

- ✔ When cleaning carpet, provide adequate ventilation to reduce the risk of mold contamination.

- ✔ Where carpets adjoin hard floors, put up caution and wet floor signs until the carpets are completely dry. Stepping from a damp, freshly cleaned carpet to a smooth, hard surface can easily result in a serious fall.

An effective green carpet-care program consists of regular daily vacuuming and spot cleaning, periodic interim maintenance, and less frequent heavy maintenance (extraction).

Your goals for interim maintenance are to reduce exposures for workers, occupants, and the environment while efficiently maintaining the appearance and life of the carpet. That means minimizing the amount of chemicals and moisture you use in the process.

If you follow the daily program, interim maintenance usually is confined to heavy traffic areas. Removing compacted soils and restoring the nap and appearance to match the surrounding areas is your goal for high-traffic areas. Traditionally, custodians have used bonnet or spin cleaning to do this, but those processes simply move most of the soil around, making the appearance uniform but accomplishing little real cleaning.

Better alternatives include light extraction — applying a small amount of traffic lane cleaner and flushing with a small amount of water with the extractor. Of course, you have to allow sufficient dry time before opening the area to traffic. Other options are dry powder cleaning, encapsulation systems, foam cleaning with a rotary brush machine, or pile lifting. Seek the advice of the green product distributor for systems that fit the needs of the building.

At some point, a deeper or more restorative cleaning likely is required. The most common method is hot water extraction.

You should develop a schedule for maintenance projects, but let the traffic and soiling of the building be the guide, not an arbitrary specification.

With proper maintenance, carpets may not need to be deep cleaned more than once a year, or in some areas, every two years. Considerations for this procedure include:

- ✔ Choose an extractor that delivers the hot water with sufficient force (PSI) to mechanically loosen compacted soils. This will reduce the amount of chemical required. Typically, portable and walk-behind units operating between 150 and 300 psi do an effective job of cleaning. For situations that frequently require heavier cleaning of compacted soils, a machine with 400 to 500 psi makes the job easier and more efficient. Ultra-high psi rates, more than 1000 psi, are designed for hard-surface cleaning and are overkill for carpets.

- ✔ Make sure the extractor removes enough of the soiled water to ensure the carpets are dry in less than 24 hours. The biggest concern when you add moisture to soiled carpet is that you're creating a perfect breeding ground for molds and mildew. Reducing potential slip-fall accidents and preventing resoiling are other important concerns. Keep in mind that *any* water left in the carpet is by definition dirty water!

- ✔ Look for carpet-cleaning tools that are ergonomically designed. Carpet cleaning is a strenuous activity. When workers are tired, they tend to rush and make mistakes, and the potential for injury skyrockets. We tell you more about choosing tools in Chapter 11.

✔ Ensure that ventilation is adequate or even increased in the areas to be cleaned. Doing so helps reduce potential exposure issues for the workers and helps the carpet dry more quickly.

✔ Evaluate some of the new technologies — low-moisture foam systems, counter-rotating brushes or microfiber rollers, encapsulation systems, and others. Equipment manufacturers are investing heavily into new machines that are more effi-cient, use fewer chemicals and less water, allow carpets to dry more quickly, are designed to be more durable and repairable, have improved ergonomics, and so on. Contact your equipment supplier and arrange for demonstrations at the building to properly evaluate options.

Carpet care relies more heavily than other cleaning concerns on occupant communication and feedback, because most spots are more easily removed when the spill is still wet. Educating occupants about how to respond to even simple spills by providing them with an internal phone number for someone to call or even directions for cleaning up small spills can go a long way toward protecting carpets and helping all occupants understand how their activities affect the indoor environment. We give you the details on communication with occupants in Chapter 9.

Food areas

Addressing cafeterias, breakrooms, and other food areas is critical for minimizing potential pest infestations. Pests are attracted to food particles, spills, sugar in empty pop cans, and so on, and they bring with them a host of illnesses and other threats to occupant health. They're also destructive to the building furnishings and the building itself.

Communication of the importance of this activity to occupants and giving them instructions on how they can help prevent infestations is a central part of this procedure. Ask them to rinse any contain-ers before placing them in the trash or recycling containers. If a refrigerator is provided for occupant use, occupants should be responsible for removing any old containers or food items and for cleaning it on a regular basis.

Paying careful attention to the hygiene in these areas and engag-ing the building occupants in the process helps reduce the need for application of extremely toxic pest-elimination chemicals. It's a critical part of a low-impact integrated pest-elimination program.

Indoor plants

If the building uses a contract service to provide and care for indoor plants, review expectations with them. Make sure that any fertilizers or pest-control products meet the green chemical standards.

If building occupants are allowed to bring their own plants into the building, the standards should be clearly spelled out and communicated. Aside from fertilizers and pesticides, other issues include ensuring that spills or overwatering are dealt with immediately, that plant containers are not in direct contact with carpets or other fabric surfaces, and that plants are not placed on ventilation or heating units.

Because green plants are an easy and low-cost way to make an office environment more comfortable, their use is often encouraged. This is an excellent topic for the steering committee to use in their communication program (see Chapter 9). While making the rules clear, the committee can reinforce their commitment to improving the indoor environment for all occupants.

Recycling

Waste can, in most cases, be turned into usable materials, and a recycling program is an incredibly effective tool for reducing humans' impact on the environment. It addresses the issues of solid waste disposal as well as reducing the need to extract raw materials to create new products. An effective recycling program can reduce solid waste disposal volume between 50 and 90 percent, which can have significant impacts on reducing the cost of waste disposal.

Participating in a recycling program lets the building's occupants be a part of the process and contribute to meeting the overall goals of reducing impacts.

Beginning a recycling program starts with two actions:

1. **Conduct an audit of the waste stream.**

   Determine exactly what is being disposed of so that you can create a plan for best reducing or eliminating it.

2. **Review the trash/recycling hauler's guidelines and requirements.**

    You might want a representative of this contractor or another vendor with expertise in recycling on your green team. Make sure they understand the commitment to the plan, and seek their guidance in developing a recycling program that fits the building.

 Track and document the results of these efforts. Reduction of waste disposal and collection of recyclable materials are key measures in evaluating overall success.

Trash

Subtle points distinguish a green trash program from the traditional. Here are a few of them:

✔ **Try to standardize the sizes of trash receptacles in the building.** Settling on a few sizes (appropriate for intended use) cuts down on the number and variety of liners that you need to purchase and inventory. Too-large bags mean a waste of plastic, and too-small bags lead to broken bags and having to double- or triple-bag the contents.

✔ **Provide separate receptacles for wet and dry trash.** Wet trash includes any food items, coffee cups, and the like. Wet-trash receptacles should have liners and be changed daily to prevent attraction of pests. Dry trash — nonrecyclable paper, staples, clips, and so on — doesn't require a liner and can be emptied less frequently. Separating wet and dry trash reduces labor costs and the number of bags you use.

 Adapting trash procedures may be a significant change in the building. Be sure that you clearly communicate the new goals and expectations to all building occupants. Almost nothing leads to a complaint more quickly than a trash can that isn't emptied.

Restrooms

The one area that generates complaints more quickly than a missed trash can is the restroom. When properly carried out, the green cleaning plan we outline in this section can go a long way toward reducing or, dare we say, eliminating restroom complaint calls while maximizing the protection of occupant and visitor health.

Outside of entryways, the restrooms are the most heavily trafficked and used area of the building. The watchwords of an effective restroom cleaning program are *frequency* and *thoroughness*. Dusting in offices once a week may be acceptable, but the restrooms in a busy building may have to be policed every three hours or even hourly.

Your survey (see Chapter 5) and careful monitoring dictate the cleaning frequency that's appropriate for the restrooms in the building.

The one place you can be certain that your green cleaning program will be judged is in the restroom. Any missteps in this area can become major setbacks for your entire program.

Begin planning restroom procedures by choosing the right chemicals. You actually need very few for daily cleaning: A general purpose cleaner, a nonacid bowl cleaner, disinfectant, and a neutral floor cleaner are the core products for restroom cleaning. Turn to Chapter 10 for more specific advice.

Traditionally, custodians have had a tendency to overuse and misuse disinfectants. Your objective is to remove soils and contaminants from surfaces. You don't need to kill all the bugs. Even if they're alive and screaming as they go down the drain, they're removed from our concern.

Harmful bacteria and high moisture levels in the restroom mean you need to pay special attention to how you use disinfectants when you do need them. You want to maximize the disinfectant's contact time to ensure that it's effective.

A typical restroom procedure may have 8 to 12 or so individual steps. In a green cleaning program, you apply disinfectants to countertops, toilets, urinals, light switches, door handles, and other surfaces that are frequently touched early in the process to maximize the contact time.

No matter what disinfectant product you decide to use, always follow the manufacturer's directions for dilution, application, dwell time, and rinsing.

The restroom is an excellent place to use premoistened microfiber cleaning cloths. Not only are they incredibly effective cleaning tools, but using them means you can avoid spraying quite so many chemicals in tight, enclosed spaces. Using fewer chemicals means reduced exposure for the worker.

You've heard it before, and it's true: A clean restroom doesn't have an odor — pleasant or unpleasant. Most fragrances added to restrooms are added to cover unpleasant odors. The result, a mix of the good and bad is usually worse than the original offensive odor. In spite of what you've heard on television, no particular scent signifies *clean*.

If strongly fragranced products are the norm in a building's restrooms, you need to re-educate the occupants. Managing their expectations may become an important part of your overall communication plan. Chapter 9 tells you more about communicating changes.

A thorough daily cleaning that addresses corners, edges, behind fixtures, under the sinks, and other fixtures, when coupled with periodic policing throughout the day results in clean, safe, and odor-free restrooms.

If the restroom is cleaned properly, and we mean *thoroughly,* but still has an odor, you have a different problem. Involve building operations or the maintenance contractor and look at drains, traps, and other places where moisture can be trapped and allow the growth of biological organisms.

The final considerations in the restroom procedure involve paper and dispenser choices. As you find out in Chapter 12, we advocate replacing all folded paper towels with roll towels. These are much less wasteful and reduce the chances of running out of paper between restroom checks.

We also recommend looking for jumbo rolls and dispensers that hold multiple rolls for the hand towels and for toilet tissue. Doing so can reduce complaints about running out of paper and reduce the number of times a roll must be replaced during the day. Larger rolls are more economical, reducing purchase and inventory costs.

When the time comes to renovate the restroom, give serious consideration to installing touch-free fixtures and dispensers. They offer the obvious benefit of reducing the potential for transmitting germs and illnesses.

Finally, growing numbers of new innovations are available for restrooms. These include biological-based cleaners and maintainers for drain lines, traps, and odor control; touch-free equipment for cleaning; steam vapor machines; touch-free faucets and flush valves; and more. Work with your janitorial supplier to stay abreast of the latest technologies as they become available.

Finding Further Opportunities

Your green cleaning program may address many other procedures; we have covered the most common and important of them, but your particular needs should be considered, as well.

A central point through most, if not all, of the procedures you use in your green cleaning program is focusing efforts to prevent the introduction of soil, capturing and containing it at the earliest and easiest stage possible, and then disposing of it properly. Doing so allows you to minimize the need for stronger chemicals and more intensive activities, and it helps control labor costs.

As you analyze other opportunities in the building, keep the original goals in mind: reducing exposures and identifying efficiencies.

Focusing on these goals and using the procedures that we discuss as a guideline helps put your green team in a good position to evaluate and modify any additional procedures the building requires.

Chapter 7

Training for Green Cleaning Programs

*G*reen cleaning procedures, which we talk about in Chapter 6, vary in small but important ways from traditional cleaning procedures; the primary difference is a shift in focus from cleaning for appearance to cleaning to protect health and the environment, and that's also true for green cleaning training programs.

Our basic advice? Don't reinvent the wheel. Assuming a building is basically well-maintained today, chances are the training programs will need some retuning, but not a major overhaul. If you aren't using a formal training program, take comfort that you can find many programs on the market. The information in this chapter (and throughout the book) helps you evaluate the various options and modify the program you choose to best fit your needs.

Excuses, excuses

One of the first comments heard when we started working in the cleaning industry was, "Our industry suffers from a lack of training programs." Throughout the ensuing 25 years we've heard the same lament over and over again. It's almost become a self-fulfilling prophecy; by repeating this over and over we seem to give ourselves permission *not* to train custodians. The problem however, is not a *lack* of training programs; it is a lack of *will* to use a training program.

(continued)

(continued)

The typical reasoning goes something like this:

I can't afford to take the time for formal training programs. The market is too competitive, clients are always looking for the lowest-priced service, my margins are too small, my budget has been slashed. Cleaning personnel turnover is too high, by the time I train a new person they've probably quit. I'd just be training my competitors' people. Besides, everyone already knows how to clean . . .

Paradoxically, the executives who make these statements also promote their services as "professional" and "cutting-edge." They talk about being in a "people" business and that their cleaning staff is their most important resource. Now, we're not making these comments to pick on or shame anyone in the cleaning industry. It's true, the industry *is* extremely competitive, turnover *is* high, margins *are* very low, and budgets *are* tight. However, an effective training program is the necessary first step in changing the situation. And trying to implement a green cleaning plan *without* an effective training program is likely to fail.

Uncovering the Value of Training

Everyone *doesn't* already know how to clean. In fact, if we cleaned an office building the same way we clean our homes, a three-hour run would likely take three days! We train custodians for the following reasons:

✔ **To ensure procedures are performed properly and safely.**

Without adequate training, the potential for job-related accidents and injuries is very high. Cleaning personnel work with highly concentrated and potentially hazardous chemicals every day and at times in confined spaces with limited ventilation. Thus, in addition to using greener chemicals, you need to ensure that staff are trained on proper dilution methods and are using the appropriate personal protective equipment. And from a building management side, you need to make sure that cleaning personnel are conducting their job with adequate ventilation in order to protect their health and that of the building occupants.

All in all, the lack of proper training is a major contributor to on-the-job injuries and the skyrocketing cost of workers' compensation. Consider the following for your crew:

- They use electrical equipment — often in wet environments — so make sure that adequate precautions are in place to protect them.

- They use, lift, push, pull, and move things that are very heavy and cumbersome, so train them to minimize risk of back and other musculoskeletal injuries — the leading cause of injuries to cleaning personnel.

- Custodians often work alone, after hours, and out of contact with supervisors or other support staff. When questions arise about using a product or piece of equipment properly, often there is no one to ask. Cleaning personnel need to know who to contact when they have a problem or question.

✔ **To engage cleaning staff in the process by helping them understand why they're directed to do certain tasks.**

You can simply order a custodian to carry out tasks with no real understanding of why she's doing what she does, but that's the least-effective form of leadership. For best results, you need to train the custodians so that they understand not only *what* they're supposed to do but *why* they're doing it. Custodians who really understand what's going on are more likely to perform well and to find solutions to problems when they occur because they understand the goal — not just the assigned task.

Fully engaged custodians, those who understand and embrace the commitment to green cleaning, will become ambassadors for your program. Your clients, the building occupants, are far more likely to encounter the custodians on a day-to-day basis than to see you. These custodians are the face of your program, products, and service. Engaged, motivated, and knowledgeable custodians portray a professional company or in-house operation. Lackadaisical, unmotivated, confused, or resentful employees don't.

✔ **To maintain and improve the green cleaning program.**

Train custodians to be your eyes and ears in the building. Show them what to look for and create the appropriate opportunities to provide feedback so you can continually improve your green cleaning program. Some of the common issues are reporting occupants who lock their offices or whose offices are so cluttered that cleaning can't be performed, identifying areas where recycling and waste management aren't being performed properly, and reporting leaking faucets and other similar issues.

✔ **To increase the professionalism of the industry through continuing education.**

Training can create some intangible and long-term benefits, especially concerning the social impacts of cleaning. Many people in the industry lament that cleaning is the bottom of the heap, relegated to the basement, unappreciated, disrespected, and doomed to low wages. If those in the cleaning industry want to be treated as professionals, they have to behave as professionals. And professionals are constantly learning and improving their skills.

Almost everyone wants to do a good job when they come to work. Very few people wake up in the morning and challenge themselves to go to work and do a poor job. Those few who do generally don't last too long anyway. But, if you don't tell your employees what a good job looks like, or how to go about doing a good job, they become frustrated very quickly.

Cleaning personnel who receive no instruction or, worse, receive conflicting instructions assume that what they do isn't important to their boss. And if it's not important to the boss, it quickly becomes less important to them. They lose interest in trying to figure out the right way to do things and just go through the motions. Soon they start looking for a better place to work, somewhere where they're appreciated and their efforts rewarded. Money is certainly an important motivator, but so is self-esteem. If a job fails to satisfy either or both needs for too long a period of time, people will move on. This is one of the primary reasons turnover is so high in this industry.

The answer isn't simply to legislate higher wages. Rather, we need to demonstrate the importance of the work being done and the skills of the people who perform it. This begins with training.

After all, the work that is being done *is* incredibly important. The whole point of a green cleaning program is to protect human health and the environment. The individuals caring for the building are directly involved with protecting your health, your children's health, and the health and well-being of every occupant and visitor to the building. In the general scheme of things, this is quite a responsibility. Isn't it worthwhile to make sure it's done properly?

The Starting Point: Defining Green Cleaning

Before you present the tasks and procedures that the cleaning personnel will use, take the time to explain what green cleaning is. Put their new jobs and responsibilities in perspective and help them understand how important their roles are. Cover the impacts of cleaning and the advantages of green cleaning versus traditional methods.

Do *not* trash our industry or condemn traditional methods. Rather, stress the benefits of new technology, scientific studies, and progress within our industry. The custodians should be proud of what they do in protecting human health and the environment.

This part of the training program doesn't have to take a long time to present. Allowing time for questions, you should be able to cover the most important points in the initial orientation in under an hour. Some of the topics to cover include:

✔ Define *green* and *green cleaning* (see Chapter 1).

✔ Explain the impacts from the cleaning industry on occupant health, as well as on the environment.

✔ Discuss any specific occupant issues within the building such as further protecting the health of children, elderly, or other vulnerable occupants, if appropriate.

✔ Provide examples of the changes that you will implement, with a particular focus on those that will make their jobs better or further protect health.

Consider creating a simple handout with Web addresses for sources of additional information. Hand these out to the individuals who express an interest in learning more about green cleaning.

Training for Green Cleaning

Greening your training program doesn't mean you have to throw out what you've been doing. Whether you're retooling your current program, building a new one, or working with someone to help you develop a training program, keep the following points in mind:

✔ **Understand that change is difficult.** Be sensitive to the custodians' concerns as the new program is being introduced.

✔ **Begin by providing the framework of why you're going green.** Explain the *whats* and *whys* of green cleaning, and what's in it for the cleaning staff — after all, green cleaning is designed to reduce impacts on their personal health and safety.

✔ **As the procedures are being introduced, take time to relate how each task impacts your green goals.** Also make sure the staff knows that this new program isn't an attempt to get them to work harder for no additional pay.

✔ **Close the loop.** Help the custodians understand how this is a shared responsibility and the value they are creating.

Some custodians may have been cleaning for many years and have developed certain assumptions that are difficult to shake. These veterans are more likely to accept change if you present it positively.

Our industry has made some remarkable technological advances in just the past few years. Generate some excitement around discovering new technologies rather than simply condemning the old ways. Remember to point out to your team members that they're major beneficiaries of this change because they'll be using safer products and better equipment.

As you train the custodians to actually perform the cleaning procedures, draw their attention to how a particular task helps meet the green goals. For example, as you demonstrate how to clean an entryway, explain that completing this task early in the shift helps reduce the amount of soil and pollutants entering your building, which then helps reduce occupant exposure to these irritants and makes their jobs easier and reduces the amount of time the custodians will have to spend dusting or sweeping in the long run.

Restrooms are a particular challenge. Most people believe that they have to kill every germ in sight to properly clean a restroom. You're likely to meet resistance when you coach the custodians when and where to use general-purpose cleaners versus disinfectants or sanitizers. Again, loop back to your initial discussions about reducing exposure and protecting health.

Overuse of disinfectants can be counterproductive in your efforts to protect health by contributing to the development and growth of more-resistant bacteria and other biological organisms. (See Chapter 10.) You should also point out that the new procedures help reduce the custodians' exposure to potentially dangerous chemical components. The same is true when you explain how to properly apply the cleaning chemical to the cloth rather than spraying the surface to be cleaned.

Throughout your training sessions, loop back to and reinforce the reasons for implementing green cleaning and the new procedures: cleaning in the most effective and efficient way while reducing the impacts of cleaning on the people doing the work, the building's occupants and visitors, and the environment.

As soon as you mention efficiency, the natural reaction is for custodians to expect wage or job cutting. Anticipate this reaction and address it head-on. By making your procedures more efficient, you're making their jobs easier to perform, and any time savings can be used to improve the overall cleaning in the building. The objective is to better use the time we have available to more effectively and thoroughly clean the building, not to reduce payroll.

Different people learn best in different ways. Some are visual learners, others respond to verbal instruction, and some really shine in an on-the-job format. Of course, you may also be confronted with employees who aren't fluent in English and may be speaking a variety of languages. There are many tools and systems available that will help you tailor your training program to fit the needs of your unique set of employees. Work with your green supplier to identify and try a variety of these tools.

Chapter 8

Stewardship and the Art of Continual Improvement

In This Chapter

▶ Keeping your program on the cutting edge

▶ Planning for program maintenance and improvement

*W*hen your communication program is in place and building occupants are taking note of the changes and reacting in a positive fashion, you really have some momentum going. And at that point you can sit back, relax, and enjoy the fruits of your labor, right? Nope.

The long-term success of all the hard work you've already done rests on planning for the future. The world is always changing, technology is changing, and your plan must allow for change and growth as well. In this chapter, we discuss two key activities that help ensure the long-term viability and success of your green cleaning plan: planning for continual improvement and developing a stewardship plan.

Striving for Continual Improvement

Over the past five to ten years, the technological improvements in chemistry, paper, and equipment for the cleaning industry have been impressive. Almost every major manufacturer now offers a line of green cleaning products, equipment, tools, or other supplies. And significant portions of their research and development money and efforts are dedicated to this arena. Our definition of green is comparative: products and services that have less impact on health and the environment than other products and services used for the same purpose.

Given that green cleaning is in a constant state of improvement and change, a key part of your program needs to be the evaluation of newer products, equipment, tools, and procedures so that you can work into your program more-effective options or those that have less impact on health and the environment. A relatively easy way to keep up with change in the industry is to establish a sub-group within your green team tasked with semi-annual or annual evaluations of new products, equipment, procedures, and services. Ask them to present their recommendations to the overall commit-tee on a regular basis. Phase in implementation as older products are used up or equipment needs to be replaced. Some specific methods these groups typically employ include:

✔ Subscribe to industry journals (see Appendix B). Many of these offer an online edition linked to more information about various topics, products, and manufacturers.

✔ Attend national and regional trade shows sponsored by the International Sanitary Supply Association (ISSA).

✔ Join cleaning and maintenance associations organized by spe-cific types of facilities or organizations such as the Building Service Contractors Association International (BSCAI), Hospitals for a Healthy Environment (H2E), or the Healthy Schools Campaign (See Appendix B.)

✔ Develop a good working relationship with suppliers. They can provide a wealth of information from the various manufactur-ers they represent.

Developing a Stewardship Plan

Stewardship recognizes that creating the healthiest indoor environ-ment possible is the responsibility of everyone in the building. Your stewardship plan is simply the document that codifies your building's green goals and policies, along with the building occu-pants' responsibilities in achieving them.

A key value of a stewardship plan is that it documents most of the issues that need to be put in place to effectively implement a green cleaning program.

Most green cleaning program stewardship plans are derived from the cleaning standard developed by American Society for Testing and Materials *(ASTM E1971: Standard Guide on Stewardship for Cleaning Commercial and Institutional Buildings)* and the U.S. Department of the Interior, which has a specific requirement to deliver a stewardship plan as part of its bid package.

Break up your stewardship plan into pieces and work your way through each, rather than trying to sit down and write the entire document at once.

Regardless of how you approach this task, we can't stress its importance too much. The stewardship plan is the underpinning of your entire green cleaning program. Shortcuts taken here make your task much more difficult, and time invested on the plan will pay off in the long run. Like every other element in this program, the stewardship plan is subject to review and improvement. Remember, you can't make it perfect, but you can make it better.

Building policy and goals statement

The first step in developing a stewardship plan is creating a specific *building policy and goals statement,* which is a brief statement that expresses a commitment to support the mission of the organization by ensuring a clean, healthy facility while protecting the health and safety of the cleaning staff and operating with environmental sensitivity. This statement essentially provides a capsule summary of your overall stewardship plan. A reader should understand *why* the plan is implemented, *what* the expected results of the plan are, and *who* is responsible for ensuring its success. Although this statement requires input from a variety of people in the building, the ultimate responsibility for writing it rests with building management.

A building policy and goals statement is generally fairly short, but resist the idea that a boilerplate or template document be tweaked for your purposes. The document is a very specific document for a specific building.

If building management fails to support and drive the creation of this document, the overall program is likely to fail. On the other hand, when building management embraces the concept and crafts a solid policy, the stage is set for a very successful green cleaning program.

Management goals

Building management goals are the targets you use to measure the success of your program. Achieving these goals is why you've embarked on this journey. These goals must be consistent with your cleaning specifications or contract. If you find they're not, you need to bring them into alignment before proceeding.

The conflict may be the result of outdated written specifications, which need to be updated reflecting the current situation. The disconnect may also highlight conflicting goals. Although that's an unusual situation, you need to resolve it to avoid problems after the plan is implemented.

Record your goals in the stewardship plan. Typically, these management goals include items such as the following:

- **Cleaning quality goals:** These may include a maximum number of complaints for a given period or target quality assurance inspection results.

- **Waste diversion goals:** This could be a target percentage of waste managed by recycling; recycling specific types of items; percentage of waste diverted by specifying packaging requirements for cleaning products, supplies, and equipment; or post-consumer waste content of janitorial paper products.

- **Worker safety goals:** Typical measures include lost days due to injury, workers' compensation claims, and minor injuries not requiring lost time.

- **Product goals:** Measures might include specifying a certain number of products to be replaced with more environmentally preferable options; transitioning targeted equipment to more ergonomic, environmentally preferable, or efficient options each year; a reduction in the number of cleaning chemicals used; and so on.

Staffing plan

The janitorial contract may already have the basics of a staffing plan in place. This is especially true if an outside contractor is used. Even if a plan is in the contract, take the time to review it and check that it includes:

- Personnel list, organized by labor category

- Descriptions of roles and responsibilities

- Training or education requirements

- Shift hours

- Specific assignments

- Any unique contract or union requirements

One of the unique features of a green cleaning program is the *green team* — the group of people responsible for drafting your stewardship plan, monitoring its progress, and making the changes necessary to ensure your program is sustainable. This team needs a leader or coordinator. Your staffing plan lists the team members and specific duties or responsibilities of the green team coordinator. These may include:

✔ Ensuring emergency preparedness and response

✔ Handling training development and document management

✔ Monitoring hazardous materials storage and waste management

✔ Tracking and reporting waste generation and recycling

✔ Leading recycling education and program promotion

✔ Evaluating cleaning chemical products for environmental preferability

✔ Issuing and using personal protection equipment guidelines

✔ Managing OSHA, HICPAC, JCAHO, and other program requirements

✔ Managing hazard communication

✔ Developing cleaning procedures and schedules

✔ Coordinating building stewardship team activities

The green team coordinator isn't an honorific position but requires a dedicated and hard-working individual. Position power may help get some things done, but choose the team leader for that person's attention to detail, organizational and communication abilities, and sincere desire to do the job. For more information on choosing this person, see Chapter 4.

Putting your green team to work

Gaining the buy-in and participation from others in your organization is critical to the success of your green cleaning program, and an important step in doing so is building a green team that is productive and motivated. The single most important qualification for members of this team is a real desire to actively participate in the program. This is a working committee.

As you read this chapter, you may come away with the impression that this is a lot of work — and you're right! Often, organizations fail to maximize the opportunity simply because the work is assigned to busy people who don't have the time to undertake such an assignment. A good plan starts small and goes slowly in a process that generates early victories and the momentum to accomplish larger steps. You can make all this easier on yourself and your team by getting outside assistance.

Some of the best — and often untapped — resources are your janitorial supply vendors. These people are highly motivated to help implement a green cleaning program. They have the skill and resources (including time) to help with the audits, develop plans, test products, train custodians, and so on. They typically will do so for no additional fees as long as the building uses their products. And the fact of the matter is that the building will buy toilet paper, cleaning chemicals, and vacuum cleaners from someone, and every janitorial supply distributor can deliver to the building. So the real value is the support necessary to help the building develop the plan and implement the program.

To get your green team up and running, follow these steps:

1. **Create the team charter.**

   The charter outlines exactly *what* the green team does. Generally, this is to give advice on environmental and cleaning issues related to building operations and to help communicate those issues to everyone in the building including all occupants, visitors, outside vendors, third-party contractors, and suppliers.

2. **Recruit team members.**

   Team members should include a broad representation from the groups of people affecting or affected by the building. Although all members of the team are important, some may serve as permanent members, and in some situations other members can participate solely when specific issues need to be addressed. For example, representatives of building management, occupants, and cleaning staff are permanent members; outside vendors and contractors may be pulled in as needed. Total membership can include:

   - Building management representatives
   - Environmental management staff
   - Cleaning staff
   - Cleaning contractor management
   - Tenant representatives
   - LEED project manager
   - Product suppliers (for example, distributors)
   - Product manufacturers
   - Outside contractors such as pest-management contractors, landscaping, HVAC and other equipment maintenance suppliers

   For more information on choosing green team members see Chapter 4.

3. **Identify the scope of issues.**

   Many organizations have numerous ongoing projects and initiatives. Thus, you need to set firm boundaries for what issues the green team will consider. These typically include:

- Cleaning standards/quality
- Indoor air quality
- Environmental aspects of cleaning operations, such as consumable products like janitorial paper, plastic liners, and so on
- Recycling efforts
- Overall communication strategies and responsibilities

4. **Set meeting frequencies.**

The size and scope of your project determines the frequency of full team meetings. Larger, more complex facilities may require more frequent meetings than small one- or two-tenant buildings.

Assign responsibilities for setting agendas, recording and distributing meeting minutes, and other internal communications to ensure the smooth functioning of the green team.

In many operations, the complexity of the tasks may require forming subgroups with specific assignments. They perform their tasks and report back to the whole team at specified times. For example, one group may be tasked with ongoing evaluations of new chemical options to meet one of the management goals.

Product criteria

Your stewardship plan details the criteria you use to evaluate cleaning products in your facility. This becomes the guideline you use for continual improvement and evaluation of new chemical options over time. We discuss cleaning-product selection in detail in Chapter 10.

Cleaning guidelines

As you develop your cleaning guidelines, be certain that they're consistent with any specific requirements in your cleaning contract or specifications. Typical topics include:

✔ Summary of cleaning tasks

- Table of tasks to be performed
- Products to be used by task
- Appropriate use of dilution equipment and concentrated products

✔ Cleaning procedures

- Task procedure guides with steps and time to complete the task

- Products to be used

- Proper mixing or dilution of concentrates

- Spill-prevention guidelines

- Personal protection equipment requirements

- Quality assurance guidelines

✔ Cleaning schedules

- Task frequencies

- Major task (floor or carpet work, for example) frequencies

- Inspection schedule for routine and periodic tasks

Safety and health program

You implement a green cleaning program to protect health, so that program certainly includes a safety and health plan. Such a plan typically has two components: accident prevention and OSHA compliance. The accident-prevention plan should include:

✔ Evaluation of equipment, tasks, and procedures for ergonomics. Many injuries are related to the use of equipment that forces the worker to move in ways that cause musculoskeletal damage over time.

✔ Training and supervision to ensure proper lifting methods are being followed and any support harnesses that are required are being used.

✔ Use of proper protective devices and methods for pouring and mixing chemicals to prevent splashes that cause eye or skin burns.

Your plan needs to address applicable OSHA requirements including:

✔ Hazard communication

✔ Personal protective equipment

✔ Respiratory protection

✔ Blood-borne pathogens

✔ Asbestos management and abatement

✔ Others related to your cleaning specifications

Hazardous materials management

Protecting building occupants and visitors from contact with hazardous materials is an important responsibility. You might tend to think of hazardous materials as exotic chemicals or radioactive materials; the reality is that *almost any* chemical in a concentrated form could be hazardous. The two important parts in this section relate to storage areas and your emergency spill response plan.

Storage areas

Your stewardship plan should include a section on storage areas. This includes areas set aside for the storage of hazardous materials that are *not* part of your cleaning operations as well as the areas provided for storing cleaning chemicals and supplies. Storage areas may be larger and centralized (often in the basement) or smaller janitor closets located throughout the building. Usually there is a combination of both types of storage areas. Make sure you include:

✔ Descriptions and maps of storage areas in use in the building

✔ Inventory of materials stored in each area

✔ Identification of incompatible materials requiring segregation

✔ Description of required standards for ventilation, secondary containment, fire rating, placarding, emergency response procedure postings, eye wash stations, spill containment kits, and instructions

Emergency spill response plan

Responding quickly and properly to a spill is the most effective way to minimize potential impact to either building occupants or the environment. Your stewardship plan should include a section on emergency spill response that includes:

✔ Internal and external (local agencies) notification numbers and responsibilities

✔ Evacuation procedures and maps

✔ Small spill clean-up procedures and responsibilities

✔ Major spill cleanup, identification of appropriate contractors, phone numbers, and responsibilities

Hazardous waste management

The most common types of hazardous wastes in typical office buildings include body fluids and specialized cleaning chemicals such as floor-finish removers (strippers), certain metal or stone polishes and sealants, and some carpet spotters. If other, less-typical forms of hazardous wastes are generated in your facility, they also should be documented in this section.

Your janitorial supply distributor should have various kits and training programs for dealing with common hazardous materials. Your safety or risk-management department likely has a great deal of information about other types of hazardous materials generated in your facility. In other words, most of the information already exists, you just need to collect it and put it in this section of the plan. Your stewardship plan will include a section detailing your plans for dealing with hazardous waste. This should include:

✔ **Identification:** Identify the types of hazardous waste generated in your building.

✔ **Containment and labeling:** The plan includes a description of proper containment and labeling of any waste generated during the cleaning of your facility. Ideally, with proper product selection, this will be minimized. However, even your green, non-hazardous product, when used to clean up a hazardous material, becomes hazardous waste. Your stewardship plan needs to consider these possibilities as well.

✔ **Disposal procedures:** The plan identifies the disposal contractor to be contacted if or when hazardous waste is generated.

Waste minimization and recycling

Much of our discussion in this chapter focuses on reducing health impacts. Of equal importance is reducing environmental impacts — making efficient use of resources, especially natural resources. Although these resources are critical for business operations, you can minimize waste and the impact on landfills as well as reduce the need for consuming additional virgin resources with effective recycling programs. Your stewardship plan should cover the following areas in the section on waste minimization and recycling:

✔ **Contract requirements.** Identify any specific contract requirements for recyclables. In addition, identify any other materials not specified in the contract that may be recycled in your geographic area. Keep in mind that markets (and prices) for recycled materials can fluctuate a great deal. Your cleaning contractor may also identify other profitable recycling opportunities and you can include these in your plan as well.

✔ **Collection procedures.**

- Map or diagram of recycling bin locations throughout the facility

- Collection frequencies

- Identification of contractors who pick up the recyclable materials and their schedules

✔ **Strategies for minimizing contamination.** One of the major hurdles to maximizing the value of recycled materials is preventing contamination. For example, one of the most valuable recycled materials is white writing paper, typically generating the most profit in a recycling program. However, when mixed with newsprint, colored paper, or even envelopes, the entire lot is valued at the least valuable material's rate. This is true even if the amount of contamination is extremely small as percentage of the total.

If your program includes selling the recycled materials, preventing contamination becomes very important. Frequent education (and re-education) of the building occupants is a necessity. You may also need to install a sorting station in the building to separate materials before they're picked up by the contractor. *Note:* Presorting may actually be a requirement in some contracts already.

✔ **Other waste minimization or diversion strategies.** These might include specifying and purchasing products that use minimal or alternative packaging materials such as bag in the box, concentrated products, packaging that contains certain percentages of recycled content, and so on.

✔ **Measurement requirements and strategies.** These might include:

- Volume measurements

- Participation measurements (percentage of tenants following the program)

- Recycled material volume trends over time

- Recycled material trends by type of materials

- Measuring these results against the goals you set early in the development of your stewardship plan

✔ **Other waste minimization opportunities.**

Communications

Communications is a very important component in your steward-ship plan. In fact, it's so important that we give it a chapter (Chapter 9) of its own. Here's a preview of the key points to include in your stewardship plan, but turn to Chapter 9 for more detail.

✔ **Tenant guidelines:** A list or definition of tenant requirements, including:

- Office spaces where eating is acceptable

- Notification of spills or cleanup of spills

- Emergency contact numbers

- Storage or use of personal cleaning products in the facility

✔ **Recycling:** The success of any recycling program depends on the occupants' understanding and following the guidelines. Experience shows that this information needs to be repeated and emphasized over and over again. New people come into the building and should have easy access to the expectations and responsibilities in the recycling efforts.

✔ **Vendor and outside contractor guidelines:** These people can have significant impacts on the indoor environment, so you want to make your expectations and procedures clear to them. For example, MSD sheets on all chemicals must be pro-vided to the green team for review and approval along with information on any unique ventilation requirements prior to their use in the building.

✔ **Custodial issues:** The plan establishes the issues that may arise in communication with custodial workers and outlines specific communication methods and tools. Opportunities for providing feedback, both positive and negative, are provided and methods to track resolution put in place. A key issue is to provide a means to resolve and prevent complaints versus assigning blame and retribution.

Goals measurement

The final piece of your stewardship plan provides the means to measure your progress. Remember the management goals you set up earlier in this chapter. Here is where you put in place the tools to measure your efforts against them.

As you develop an implementation and stewardship plan, the importance of what you're doing may seem obvious. As you make progress, you and your team are likely to see the positive results and think they're obvious to everyone. The reality is that most of the positive results will *not* be obviously tied to your efforts. When the time comes to justify your program, its continued funding, and the implementation of future enhancements you will need ammunition. Demonstrating your plan's success against the management goals will be that ammunition. Measure your progress in a document that outlines:

- ✔ **Tracking:** Identify the goal being measured, how you will measure progress, and at what frequency you'll take these measurements. For example, a goal might be to maintain tenant complaints at a level of fewer than ten per quarter. Track this measure by logging all complaints and providing a quarterly report of the totals.

- ✔ **Reporting methods:** Identify the reports, charts, and supporting materials that will allow you to share your results. Also consider who the information is to be shared with, from the stewardship team to building occupants, prospective tenants, employees, outside vendors, and so on.

- ✔ **Reporting frequencies:** Strike a balance between allowing enough time to gather meaningful information and the importance of keeping the team and building occupants aware of progress and feeling their efforts are paying off.

Chapter 9

Getting Everyone in the Loop, and Keeping Them There

In This Chapter

▶ Identifying the goals of communication

▶ Unveiling your green cleaning program

▶ Announcing cleaning events

▶ Getting building occupants up to speed

▶ Training outside vendors and contractors

As we explain in Chapter 8, the activities of occupants, visitors, and outside contractors can have an enormous impact on a building and the requirements to keep it clean, safe, and healthy. Occupants, visitors, and contractors need to recognize how their activities can affect others and what they can do to reduce impacts on health and the environment. That's where a solid communication plan comes in.

Communication helps ensure occupants' buy-in and also helps you to achieve the best results for your green cleaning program. In fact, communication is so important that we originally considered adding a communication section to each chapter. However, sanity prevailed and we decided to dedicate a unique chapter to this topic. In this chapter we look at:

✔ Communicating the introduction of a green cleaning program

✔ Communicating major events such as strip-outs, pesticide application, elevator maintenance, and so on

✔ Occupant "training"

✔ Communicating with outside vendors

After you get started, make sure you keep the communication going. We try to give you a variety of opportunities to communicate. However, it's up to you to keep the communication at the right level and in as many different forms as possible to maintain interest in your program.

Who Talks to Whom and How: A Communications Primer

 Successful implementation of a stewardship plan depends on everyone understanding and carrying out their individual parts of the whole plan. Therefore, your central communications goal is to ensure everyone *understands* their roles and responsibilities. The better they understand the overall plan and how their efforts fit into the success of the plan, the more likely you are to succeed.

The general guideline for most of the communications is to be positive. We can't overemphasize how important this is. Introducing a green cleaning program — whether it's a comprehensive program including all chemicals, paper, liners, tools, powered equipment, training, and so on, or just replacing toilet paper with recycled content as a first step in the journey — the message is that you're trying to make the building better and *not* that the building was doing something bad that needed to be fixed.

 Developing an overall theme or "brand" for the green cleaning program is important. Organizations often develop unique names for their programs or tie them into existing programs, such as those connected to sustainability, health and safety, continual improvement, or corporate responsibility.

Communications media

You can choose from a wide variety of ways to get your message out. In fact, the only real limitation is your imagination. Some typical examples include:

- ✔ Articles in a company or facility newsletter
- ✔ Flyers and posters
- ✔ Periodic e-mails
- ✔ Programs sponsored by the Health and Safety Committee
- ✔ Tent cards on conference and cafeteria tables or reception counters

> ✔ Door hangers
>
> ✔ Small decals on doors or restroom mirrors
>
> ✔ Stickers on paper towel and toilet tissue dispensers

We provide more examples in the various sections of this chapter. The key point is to be creative. Look for novel ways to catch the occupants' attention. E-mails can be effective, but let's face it, we all get too many e-mails every day to pay attention to each of them. So, challenge your team to look for new tools and make sure your message is heard.

Communication responsibility

Communication is too important to be left to chance. In fact, we feel that communication is so important it should be the responsibility of the green team. This responsibility needs to be written into the team's charter during the initial implementation phase. (Turn to Chapters 4 and 8 to find out more about building your green team.)

Why are we making such a big issue of this? Because it's all too easy to let this matter fall back onto the cleaning staff. For example, we traditionally make changes such as switching to new products with different fragrances and waiting for complaints to come in about that new scent or something unusual happening in the building. Inevitably, the finger gets pointed at the cleaners. It is much more effective to be proactive and communicate upfront with the occupants so that they can anticipate the change and view it as a positive rather than a negative. Doing so also preempts complaints.

Introducing a Green Cleaning Program

Change can be difficult, and the occupants of your building won't necessarily believe that the changes you're making are good. We're talking about some significant changes here, so it's important to get out in front of things and let people know what's going to happen, why it's happening, and why it's good that this is happening.

As you introduce a green cleaning program, tell people about how important cleaning is in general. Many of your building's occupants probably think of cleaning as little more than pulling the trash, replacing the paper towels, and vacuuming up the stray bits of paper on the carpet. This is your chance to really explain the *value* of cleaning in general. After all, you're protecting the occupants' health, and with green cleaning in particular, you're also reducing the impact on the environment. Frankly, this is pretty powerful stuff, and you should take this chance to let occupants know what you're doing for them.

The following topics are some you might want to consider for communicating during the building's program startup.

Stressing improvement

As you introduce your green cleaning program, you need to explain *how* the products, services, procedures, and strategies in the plan reduce the impact on health and the environment compared to traditional cleaning services.

Emphasize that you are *not* making these changes because the current program is bad but because the green program is *better* than what you've been able to do in the past. And it's better because of the improvements in technologies over the past several years and your desire to continually work to create a cleaner, safer, healthier environment for the occupants.

As you communicate the benefits of your green cleaning program, stress the health benefits first. The building occupants want to know what's in it for them. After everyone understands how this plan helps them, talk about the reduced impact on the environment.

As tree-huggers ourselves, we certainly aren't trying to slight the importance of reducing cleaning's impact on the environment. However, whatever we do that impacts the environment also impacts human health.

During the initial planning stage of the program, you may have conducted occupant surveys. If so, make sure your earliest communication provides feedback based on those surveys. Doing so demonstrates that not only are you listening to their issues and concerns, but that you have addressed them in your plan. This is critical for getting buy-in and support for moving forward.

Setting expectations

As you introduce your green cleaning program, you have your best opportunity to set realistic expectations. We suggest the following motto: "We can't make it perfect, but we *can* make it better."

People in the building who suffer from asthma, allergies, or other respiratory problems, for example, may think this new program will fix everything, and that they'll have no more problems. That would be wonderful but likely won't happen. Their specific problem may not actually be a result of any cleaning operation or impacted by better cleaning. It may be that there is simply no way to effectively meet all of their needs.

The point is, your green cleaning program will make things better, we hope *much* better, but you can't make things perfect. Giving building occupants realistic expectations helps set up you and your team for success.

Explaining the changes

Okay. So you have this shiny new program and it's supposed to make things better. But what exactly does that mean? What are you doing differently and why is that better for your occupants? These are the questions your audience really wants answered. As changes are communicated, you don't have to write a book. (We've done that for you.) But briefly tell occupants about key changes in products, equipment, or procedures that they may see or that could have an impact on them. For example:

- New vacuum cleaners with improved filtration capabilities help keep microscopic dust out of the air, making it easier for everyone to breathe.

- Replacing traditional dust mops with microfiber mops or vacuum cleaners captures more of the fine dust particles before they can be kicked into the air and inhaled into the lungs.

- Replacing aerosols with trigger sprayers (and eliminating cleaning products brought from home) keeps fine droplets of chemicals from becoming airborne and makes the air cleaner and safer.

- Changing some cleaning chemicals and paper products reduces the potential impact on the environment, which is not only good in itself but has positive impacts on anyone who enjoys the outdoors, fishing, hunting, or simply breathing.

When you go through the list of products, equipment, and procedures you're implementing, you come up with a long list of potential communication points. Review the sections in this book about choosing cleaning chemicals, equipment, paper, and procedures, and you find the raw material you need for an effective series of communication pieces.

Communicating Major Events

After you have introduced your green cleaning program, the communication efforts don't end but shift focus: *What and why* become *what and when*.

In the initial communications you explain that cleaning has an impact on health, so it's important that you let people know when you're planning to conduct major cleaning activities that they're likely to smell, see, hear, notice, or otherwise be affected by. We're talking about activities like the following:

- ✔ Hard floor work, such as deep scrubs and recoats or strip-outs

- ✔ Significant carpet spotting

- ✔ Carpet shampooing or extraction

- ✔ Application of pesticides

- ✔ Application of fertilizers or weed killers

- ✔ Wall washing

- ✔ Ceiling tile cleaning

- ✔ Deep cleaning of restrooms

In many cases, you want to inform the occupants well before you begin these activities. Doing so is especially important when you're dealing with vulnerable populations but is a courtesy for all occupants and a requirement of programs such as those in the U.S. Green Building Council's Leadership in Energy and Environmental Design for Existing Buildings (LEED for Existing Buildings) and the Healthy Schools Campaign's Quick & Easy Guide to Green Cleaning in Schools (See Appendix A).

In addition to typical cleaning activities or green cleaning activities, communicate about any activities that impact the occupants' environment. The easiest way to determine what's communication-worthy is to ask yourself, "Will someone in the building notice that something has changed when this happens?" If the answer is yes, then you should provide proactive information to alert and inform the occupants about the activity.

Some examples include a strange smell from roofing or parking lot maintenance, or adjustments to the HVAC system that could let additional dust into the air or cause temperature or humidity fluctuations. Work being done on the elevator or escalator may involve using solvents or lubricants that have significant VOCs or create a lingering odor.

One of your goals is to let the occupants know *before* a major activity so they can take any appropriate steps required to minimize the impact on themselves. And these communications should be undertaken by the green team to help ensure that they're done and that they receive the attention they require.

Maximizing Positive Communication Opportunities

Far too many managers in the cleaning industry operate under the "no news is good news" paradigm. As most successful managers have discovered, that notion just isn't so. As a communication plan, waiting for bad news and then trying to fix it leads to becoming associated solely with bad news. You want just the opposite.

You need to celebrate your successes. Don't hide under a rock — be proud of what you're accomplishing and wave your flag. Make some noise. Frankly, the more people understand the benefits of what you're accomplishing and the value of green cleaning, the more they're willing to pay for results. And just think what you could do if people were willing to clean just 25 percent more than they do today!

You and the green team are charged not only with communicating what you're doing and why, but the positive results you're achieving. This is because the positive impacts of what you're doing are not always readily obvious. People notice a new smell or an odor, but they don't notice the *absence* of an odor. The building occupants aren't likely to associate a general feeling of "wellness" that develops over time because of the way you're cleaning the building. And it's hard for them to "see" how you're reducing environmental impacts. It's up to *you* to draw their attention to the positive impacts and take credit for what you accomplish.

Rather than simply running up and down the halls patting yourself on the back, look for opportunities to bring your message to the occupants. Examples include Earth Day celebrations, recycling events, "clean out the files" day, health and safety fairs, and fliers with tips people can use at home to improve their lifestyle and protect the environment. Don't overlook opportunities like these to tie your efforts to the larger picture.

Training Building Occupants

By reading this book and referring to many of the resources we discuss, you're discovering your role in creating a healthier environment. The occupants of your building need training as well. They need to understand their roles and responsibilities to make this program successful. We refer to this as shared responsibility; we're all in this together, and that's the overall theme of occupant training.

You can present this information in a variety of ways. As with any communication, the green team should find creative ways to provide training — traditional classroom events, seminars, Webinars, brown-bag luncheons, expert speakers, newsletters, articles, and the list goes on. The opportunities are endless; using a variety of frequent, short, and targeted bursts of information generates the best results. Key issues to cover include the following:

- ✔ **Tenant activities:** Many buildings have multiple tenants, and these tenants may engage in a wide range of activities from operating a day care center to running a repair center, and so on. These activities may impact occupants in the building that have nothing to do with the business. At the very least they're all likely connected to the same HVAC system and share the same entrances and common areas.

 You need to make all of the tenants aware of how their activities impact the health of the building's occupants and visitors, as well as the environment beyond the confines of their space.

- ✔ **Spills:** All building occupants need to understand that the longer a spill is left before it's cleaned, the harder it is to clean. Often what could be simply wiped up is left for the night cleaner and therefore becomes a stain that requires a powerful chemical to remove.

 Make sure occupants understand who and when to call to report spills. This also helps prevent potential slip-fall accidents and resulting lawsuits.

- ✔ **Eating in the workplace:** In an ideal world no one would eat at their desk. Realistically, it happens.

 Make sure occupants understand the impact of eating at their desks and leaving crumbs on the floor or dirty dishes in waste baskets. These habits create excellent food sources for pests and attract them in droves. The result is that pest-elimination chemicals — which can be hazardous to health — become necessary.

If occupants understand the issue and ensure their areas are cleaned after they eat, with dishes and utensils returned to the kitchen or snack area, they help prevent the need for more aggressive action. Building management needs to be aware of this issue as well, because the extra time required to clean up after people who eat at their desks impacts the time available for normal cleaning duties. And occupants need to understand who and when to call to report food spills.

✔ **Bringing cleaning products from home:** Consumer products aren't necessarily *bad* cleaners or ineffective tools. However, many of these products contain the very components you're trying to reduce or eliminate. They also aren't approved for commercial use and don't have the Material Safety Data (MSD) sheets required by the Occupational and Safety Health Administration (OSHA).

If your cleaning plan has been properly designed and funded, no one should need to bring products from home to clean her own space. But when an individual expresses the desire to do some extra cleaning in her area, consider offering her a microfiber cloth (which can be effective without chemicals) or a green cleaning product in a properly labeled refillable trigger sprayer.

✔ **Locked offices:** Of course you need to be sensitive to security issues that may require certain areas to be locked, but you need also to remember that these areas are connected to the rest of the building through the HVAC system. Thus, provisions need to be made to clean these areas on a regular basis to prevent possible buildup and transmission of dust and other contaminants that put everyone's health at risk when they accumulate in the carpets, on the desks, and so on.

Whether this means identifying a specific day for cleaning these areas and designating a specific individual to clean them, posting a security guard during cleaning operations, or some other measure, cleaning must happen in these areas. You don't want to compromise security, but you can't compromise health for security. Fortunately you can address them simultaneously.

✔ **Recycling:** Recycling is an important part of a green cleaning program, and in some cases it can be a profit center.

Be sure you're familiar with the actual requirements of the program. Traditionally, occupants have had to separate paper, cardboard, and so on into different containers. In many cases separating materials is no longer necessary. The actual sorting is done at a recycling center. Make sure your building occupants know their roles in the process.

> We've been in buildings where the occupants scoffed at the recycling program (and by extension the overall green program) because they didn't have blue trash containers for recycling. In their minds, no recycling program was in place. In fact, the building was making money with the recycling program! It was simply a lack of communication. Not only did the occupants not know about the program, the team missed a great chance to celebrate a rousing success!

Communications with Vendors and Contractors

Our theme of shared responsibility applies to visitors and outside vendors, as well as the building occupants. The first step in getting these people in the green loop is to define a policy for vendors, outside contractors, and visitors that helps ensure minimal impact on occupant health and the environment when they are working in or using the building. This policy needs to include the types of products that are allowed to be used, when various services may be performed, and how plans for these activities will be communicated to building management, visitors, and the occupants.

However, just having a policy isn't enough. You need to educate vendors and outside contractors about how their activities can impact the building occupants and the environment. They also need to understand the goals of the green program and how they fit in. Ideally, you will have representatives of the major contractors on the green team or at least accessible during periods of construction or when their work may affect the building occupants.

When vendors and contractors are a part of the team, they have a vested interest in meeting your goals — they become shared goals — and potential negative impacts are significantly reduced, especially those that are inadvertent or the result of a misunderstanding. Furthermore, these folks can provide training to you, your staff, and others, which can help reduce the need for their restorative services by improving preventative maintenance. Finally, they can even help shoulder some of the communication burden.

Examples of issues to address with vendors and so on include:

- ✔ Policies for visitors and others using the building. You want to make sure these folks know:

    - The requirements for resetting chairs, tables, and other items after meetings are over.

    - Who is responsible for cleaning the area at the end of the event.

    - Whom to call in the event of a spill.

    - How they can participate in the building's recycling program.

    - What kind of cleaning products and other items they can use inside the building.

- ✔ Policies for pest management, roofing, mechanical, construction, and other contractors who use chemicals that might affect the health of building occupants. Require Material Safety Data Sheets for all chemicals prior to work being conducted. In addition, the contractor should provide notification to the green team for distribution to occupants before they use hazardous materials such as pesticides indoors.

Part III
The Green Cleaning Tool Box

"Okay – we may need to switch to a more environmentally friendly cleaning system. Or else the 'Dissolve' transition in my presentation needs adjusting."

In this part . . .

Green cleaning programs are much more than product issues, but your green cleaning plan most likely includes changing to at least some new products, equipment, paper, and other cleaning supplies.

Just five years ago, buying green cleaning products was extremely difficult. Many early green products either didn't perform as well as their conventional counterparts or were significantly more expensive. There were no agreed-upon standards for what constituted a "green" product, and there were, unfortunately, many spurious claims. Today however, standards do exist. Products that meet the standards and perform at least as well as conventional products are readily available at competitive price points. This part lays the groundwork for a comprehensive purchasing program and helps you choose green products. In it, we look at the ins and outs of choosing chemicals, paper, equipment, entryway mats, and other janitorial supplies.

Chapter 10

Choosing Green Cleaning Chemicals

*T*hroughout this book, we have made the point that green cleaning is much more than switching to a different cleaning chemical. And it is. However, choosing the right cleaning chemicals is an important part of the whole program and a logical place to start your journey. In this chapter, we cover what you need to know to take on this aspect of your green cleaning program, from tackling myths about green chemicals to the future of green products.

Dispelling Two Pervasive Myths

Like any shift in thinking, the green cleaning movement has taken some years to take hold, and along its path has inspired some notions that simply aren't true. Here are two of the myths that arose around green cleaning, and our analysis of how much water they hold.

Myth #1: Green products don't work

At one time or another, you've probably heard (or said) that green cleaning chemicals simply don't work as well as traditional products. This was usually pointed out after some huckster claimed his product was so safe he could drink it. How could anything that innocuous be an effective cleaner?

Just five to ten years ago, the perception that green products were largely ineffective was for the most part true. Much of what was sold as "green" or "environmentally safe" was little more than colored water, especially if it was comparatively priced with traditional products. However, today the reality is quite different.

Almost every major cleaning manufacturer offers at least a basic line of green cleaning products. In fact, many of these manufacturers are investing more research and development dollars and efforts in green products than in traditional cleaners, and their green lines represent the cutting edge of cleaning technology.

What drives progress in green cleaning progress? Demand. Manufacturers make products they believe people will buy. In Chapter 1, we talk about the growing demand for green buildings. Whether driven by government regulations or increased profitability from energy, water, and other savings, companies are building green. In Chapter 2, we look at the impacts cleaning has on buildings, people, and the environment. More companies are realizing that although building green can demonstrate an excellent return on investment, managing green can be even more lucrative. Thus, they're moving their focus to green operations, including cleaning. As they do, the demand for green cleaning continues to grow, and the manufacturers are responding with more and better products.

Myth #2: Green cleaning costs more

Another myth is that green cleaning chemicals cost more than traditional products. Again, not too long ago this was true. With relatively few green products on the market, and fewer still that actually worked, manufacturers could and did charge a premium for those that actually worked.

In some cases, prices were high simply because the manufacturers were increasing profit margins. In most cases, though, the costs were higher because the demand was smaller. The economies of scale drove costs higher as manufacturers tried to recoup the higher costs for buying smaller quantities of raw materials, operating shorter and less-efficient production runs, investing in research and development, and so on.

Increasing demand for green cleaning has resulted in more manufacturers entering the green market with larger and deeper lines of products. Almost every major manufacturer has a green product line. Increased competition has driven prices down to the point where green cleaning chemicals are essentially priced at parity with traditional products. And because of the increased research and development spending, the newer products use more-efficient technologies, which often lead to significantly lower in-use costs for green products versus traditional cleaners.

Introducing Green Cleaning Standards

With all the competition that exists now, the green cleaning product marketplace can be confusing. A quick look at the manufacturers' brochures can have your head swimming. Relax; some very effective standards and tools are available to help you make informed choices. As we discuss each category of green chemical, we look also at the standards that can be used to guide your decision making.

Before we jump into the product categories and certifying organizations, a word about manufacturers' "self-certification." The use of independent third-party certifiers simply makes identifying green products easier for product purchasers. However, manufacturers who choose not to use a third party to certify their products may indeed offer products with important health and environmental benefits. The only caveat is that the test data must be reviewed to ensure that the testing has actually been performed. Unlike the pharmaceutical industry, where strict testing is required by law, health and safety testing requirements for new cleaning products are virtually nonexistent. But a manufacturer who indeed can provide evidence that the product has been tested to confirm that it in fact reduces impacts to health and the environment compared to traditional products should be considered green without the use of the third-party certifier.

In this section we briefly look at the two major standards-setting organizations in our industry: Green Seal and Environmental Choice. These organizations are those most commonly referenced in the various green building programs. In addition to these organizations, we also discuss other important programs that can affect the selection of green cleaning chemicals. To find out more about these and other oragnizations that set green standards, see Appendix A.

More than three dozen labelling programs now exist worldwide. The Global EcoLabelling Network is an international association of ecolabelling programs, including Green Seal and the Environmental Choice Program.

All of the programs mentioned in this section are voluntary; products don't have to be certified. Many manufacturers choose to self-certify their products, meaning that they do their own testing to proclaim that their products are green.

We don't mean to imply that one standard is better than another's. The real issue is that if you start with a standard, you can narrow your product choices down to a manageable number without having to learn the science of health and environmental protection. From there, of course, you need to consider the factors you would normally evaluate — performance, fit with your program, support, cost, and so on. The most important point to take away from this section is that your decision-making process is much easier when you begin your search for cleaning chemicals by looking for certification marks. If a product carries one of these marks, you can be assured it performs as the label says it will and meets the current green standards.

Green Seal

Green Seal is a nonprofit organization devoted to environmental standard setting, product certification, and public education. Green Seal's mission is to work toward environmental sustainability by identifying and promoting environmentally responsible products, purchasing, and production.

Through its standard setting, certification, and education programs, Green Seal:

- ✔ Identifies products that are designed and manufactured in an environmentally responsible manner

- ✔ Offers scientific analyses to help consumers make educated purchasing decisions regarding environmental impacts

- ✔ Ensures consumers that any product bearing the Green Seal Certification Mark has earned the right to use it

- ✔ Encourages manufacturers to develop new products that are significantly less damaging to the environment than their predecessors

The intent of Green Seal's environmental requirements is to reduce — to the extent technologically and economically feasible — the environmental impacts associated with the manufacture, use, and disposal of products. Set on a category-by-category basis, the organization's environmental standards focus on significant opportunities to reduce a product's environmental impacts.

Green Seal offers certification to all products that meet its standards. Manufacturers may submit their products for evaluation by Green Seal. Those that comply with Green Seal's requirements may be authorized to use the Green Seal Certification Mark on products and in product advertising. Manufacturers authorized to use the Green Seal Certification Mark on their product are subject to an ongoing program of testing, inspection, and enforcement.

Environmental Choice

The Environmental Choice Program (ECP), Environment Canada's ecolabelling program, offers its EcoLogo to manufacturers and suppliers who make their products and services as green as possible, according to the organization's standards. Doing so helps consumers identify products and services that are less harmful to the environment.

Established in 1988, the ECP was the second national ecolabelling initiative undertaken. A key aspect of the certification process is that it requires third-party verification of compliance to ECP certification criteria. This process ensures the program's credibility and includes:

- ✔ A review of each applicant company's product and process information

- ✔ An examination of the company's quality assurance (QA) and quality control (QC) measures

- ✔ An audit of the company's facilities for purposes of initial certification (when such is deemed necessary by ECP officials)

Currently, the Environmental Choice Program covers a number of products in the cleaning industry, including janitorial paper products, cleaning chemicals, and bacteria/enzyme-based products.

Greenguard Environmental Institute (GEI)

Another nonprofit, independent organization involved in standard setting is the Greenguard Environmental Institute (GEI). With a focus on improving indoor air quality, GEI sets acceptable standards for indoor products, buildings, and environments to positively impact quality of life and public health.

GEI has recently introduced a certification program specific to the cleaning industry that measures chemical cleaning product emissions during use.

EPA's Design for the Environment Formulator Partnership

A voluntary partnership program from the EPA, the Design for the Environment (DfE) program works to make products and processes healthier for humans and the environment. Unlike the other programs we mention in this chapter, the DfE program doesn't revolve around a specific standard, but rather works with individual manufacturers to improve their unique products.

Making the Case for Green Cleaning Chemicals

Traditional products aren't necessarily bad, but green or environmentally preferable products make use of newer technologies to create effective products at a competitive price while reducing health and environmental impacts.

So what makes a cleaner a green product? Many traditional cleaners including glass, all-purpose, carpet extraction, and washroom cleaners are known to have a variety of health and environmental problems associated with them. And although there is no such thing as zero risk (everything has some potential to cause harm), green products reduce the potential for harm to take place compared to traditional products used for the same purpose.

For example, many traditional cleaners contain 2-butoxyethanol (CAS 111-76-2), often referred to as a *butyl cleaner*. This solvent is very effective but, among other concerns, is suspected of being a developmental, endocrine, and reproductive toxicant as it passes through the skin and enters the body. In addition, many traditional detergent-based cleaners contain nonylphenol ethoxylate surfactants (CAS 9016-45-9). These surfactants are suspected to be endocrine disruptors that can cause serious problems including hypothyroidism, diabetes, hypoglycemia, reproductive disorders, and cancer.

Focusing on concentration

When you're shopping for products, make sure you look for concentrated versions. From a green cleaning perspective, concentrated products have clear advantages over their ready-to-use counterparts. They reduce environmental impacts by reduction of packaging materials, transportation impacts, and disposal impacts. And, by isolating the user from the chemical through portion-control systems, they reduce potential impacts to cleaning staff and building occupants.

Furthermore, concentrates can save money! Your choice of dispensing equipment, premeasured packets, sachets, and so on, should be guided by the specific situations in the building. You will find every manufacturer of green chemicals offering at least one type of dispensing option.

One caveat: Make sure you use some type of portion control to avoid exposure to the concentrated chemical and to avoid waste or damage to materials.

From an environmental point of view, most traditional cleaners are derived from petroleum, a valuable but limited and nonrenewable natural resource. As a society, we have come to realize that we are not being responsible stewards of this planet if we deplete nonrenewable natural resources so that future generations will never be able to use them. Beyond the sustainability issue, many of these products emit volatile organic compounds (VOCs) that can cause respiratory and other problems to the occupants of a building and the person doing the cleaning. After these VOCs are exhausted to the outdoors, they can contribute to atmospheric smog formation.

We don't want to go on and on about the potential problems associated with traditional products but to drive home the point that new technologies are now available. These new technologies clean as effectively and cost about the same as the traditional products but reduce the potential for causing harm to human health as well as the environment, and can contribute to a more sustainable future. Many building managers simply would prefer their use compared to traditional products.

 General-purpose, glass, restroom (except disinfectants), and carpet cleaners certified by Green Seal, Environmental Choice, or EPA's DfE Program are the ones that many established green cleaning programs turn to. Working with these approved lists can simplify your product evaluation process. Each organization lists products that have been submitted and approved for certification. (For more information, see Appendix A.)

Running Down Additional Green Chemicals

Now that you've decided to go green, here's the information you need to sift through the myriad options for cleaning every surface in any building you may find yourself in.

Floor-care products

Many traditional floor finishes contain ingredients such as zinc (used to crosslink the polymer making it more durable and chemical resistant), phthalates (which are used to help make the polymer flexible so it doesn't powder), solvents, and flourosurfactants (used for a variety of functions including improving application and leveling of the finish itself).

These components have definitely improved the performance of modern finishes compared to the natural waxes that they replaced beginning in the 1950s. Unfortunately, in the past several years we've learned that these same ingredients can contribute to health and environmental concerns.

Traditional strippers contain ingredients such 2-butoxyethanol, ammonia, sodium hydroxide, and akylphenol ethoxylate surfactants all of which are known to cause health and environmental problems.

New technologies are available to protect the floor, maintain appearances, and provide effective slip resistance. Using these newer technologies, manufacturers have created products that are cost competitive, similar in application, and which further reduce the potential for harm to both occupant and product users' health as well as to the environment.

Choosing the right floor-care system for your facility involves balancing several factors. After identifying a few potential candidates, we suggest conducting performance tests *in your facility*. Have your floor crew apply the test products in several typical traffic areas throughout the building and evaluate their performance over time. As appearance levels begin to decline (typically in 30 to 90 days) you will be in a position to decide which system best meets your building's needs.

Some of the factors to evaluate as you begin to identify potential products and systems include:

- ✔ Eliminating the use of heavy metals (such as zinc), phthalates, and solvents whenever possible.

- ✔ Matching the least-caustic stripper that effectively removes the chosen finish.

- ✔ Desired appearance level (gloss).

- ✔ The ability of the finish to deliver needed gloss level with fewer coats, for instance building gloss with three or four coats versus seven or eight.

- ✔ Identifying a finish that will maintain its appearance in the traffic experienced in your facility with minimal or no burnishing.

- ✔ Application methods, daily maintenance requirements, and "ease of use" must fit within the capabilities and resources of your staff.

The Green Seal Standard for floor care products is GS-40. Products that have been tested and certified may be found by visiting www.greenseal.org/findaproduct/index.cfm. This standard provides an excellent starting point in identifying potential systems.

There is a major difference when choosing a green floor care system compared to choosing other products. The key factor that differentiates green floor care from cleaners is that green floor care is a *system* — not just a collection of individual products. You need to match the green floor finish with the green stripper, as well as the suggested cleaner, and maintainer if one is recommended.

Many people believe that manufacturers specify their floor cleaner simply to sell more "juice." Certainly, they do want to sell more products, but products based on the newer technology really are designed to work most effectively as a system.

 The system approach is very important for maximizing the reduction in health and environmental impacts. Perhaps the most important thing you can do is to implement a floor-care program that reduces the frequency of burnishing, recoating, and stripping and refinishing.

In addition to reducing the health and environmental impacts of the floor finish and stripper itself, a well-designed floor-care system lasts longer. Simply put, if you can reduce the frequency of stripping and recoating from two times a year to one time per year — or better yet, once every two or three years — you will have significantly reduced the impacts associated with floor care.

Reducing or eliminating burnishing the finish cuts down the addition of dust in your building. Burnishing is an abrasive process that creates a tremendous amount of dust. If it isn't collected by an on-board vacuum system, this dust is inhaled by the operator, captured by the HVAC system, and distributed throughout the building. Obviously, this dust has to be removed, meaning increased cleaning and more frequent filter changes.

Although we're focused on the chemical part of the equation at this point, a green floor-care program includes:

✔ Effective matting (see Chapter 13)

✔ Microfiber mops (see Chapter 14)

✔ Vacuum attachments for any powered equipment

It should be clear that an effective green floor-care system will help reduce health and environmental impacts, and also help reduce or control labor costs. This is certainly a true win-win situation!

Disinfectants and sanitizers

Technically there is no such thing as a "safe" disinfectant or sanitizer. These products are pesticides and therefore toxic by definition. After all, they're specifically designed to kill living things and/or prevent them from reproducing.

Although disinfectants and sanitizers are an important tool in our toolbox to protect public health, there's a growing concern that they're being overused. In extreme cases, overuse of disinfectants and sanitizers can contribute to the creation of more-resistant bacteria, the so-called "super bugs." In some cases, serious potential health and environmental problems are associated with these products.

Before selecting the greenest alternative, consider opportunities to reduce the use of these products. In many cases a detergent-based cleaner is all you need to remove the soils (which will also remove the harmful organism), reserving the disinfectants and sanitizers only for areas of increased risk (see Chapter 6). After all, your objective is to remove the harmful organism; if it isn't dead when it goes down the drain that really isn't a problem.

No standards or certification programs exist for this category of products, so how do you know a disinfectant or sanitizer is green?

Because a product is green when its impact on health and the environment is less than that of comparable products used for the same purpose, think of products on a spectrum. Some are more hazardous to health and/or the environment and others less so. Your goal in selecting a green disinfectant or sanitizer is to move from a more-hazardous product to a less-hazardous alternative.

Here's a breakdown of the spectrum of disinfectants and sanitizers:

✔ **Sodium hypochlorite or chlorine bleach** is extremely effective against harmful organisms, but it's also a known respiratory irritant, burns eyes and skin, and if accidentally mixed with other common cleaning products will produce a poisonous gas.

If you're using chlorine bleach, a greener alternative is a comparable performing disinfectant/sanitizer, approved by the EPA that kills the target organisms, but does so without being a respiratory irritant, corrosive to eyes or skin, or one that does not produce a poisonous gas upon mixing with other cleaning agents.

✔ **Phenol-based disinfectants** are still common, especially as part of OSHA's Blood Borne Pathogen Standard. Phenols (CAS #108-95-2) are suspected of being a developmental, reproductive, respiratory, and major organ toxicant. And they frequently have a high pH, making them corrosive to eyes and skin as well as potentially damaging to floor finishes and other surfaces.

If you're using a phenol-based disinfectant, a greener alternative would be a comparable performing product approved by the EPA that kills the target organisms, but does so without having the same health concerns or damaging finishes. And as far as the Blood Borne Pathogen Standard, a greener alternative would be a product that has been proven effective against HIV-1 and Hepatitis B (HBV) but with reduced impacts on health and the environment.

✔ **Quat-based disinfectants** and sanitizers have reduced health impacts compared to bleach and phenols, although they may cause asthma. Quats are also considered to be toxic to aquatic life. And because of the wide array of formulations that use quats as the active ingredient, the final disinfectant product may have an extreme pH, which can cause eye and skin irritation, and be high in volatile organic compounds (VOCs) from added fragrances, contributing to respiratory irritation.

If you're using a quat-based disinfectant, a greener alternative would be a comparable-performing disinfectant/sanitizer approved by the EPA that kills the target organisms, but does so without being toxic to aquatic life or causing asthma. Plus, depending on the other attributes such as pH, VOCs, fragrances, surfactant package such as the use of a nonylphenol ethoxylate, and so on, you may have other opportunities to replace the disinfectant/sanitizer with an alternative that further reduces impacts on health and the environment.

✔ **Hydrogen peroxide-based sanitizers** have an improved health and environmental profile compared to most other disinfectants and sanitizers. However, these products are typically sanitizers and not disinfectants, and may not be appropriate in high-risk applications. They may be preferable in many general applications where a sanitizer would be preferable compared to a detergent-based cleaner, such as surfaces that are frequently touched or as an added safeguard around occupants with diminished immune systems.

Disinfectants and sanitizers are one of the best categories of products to help us remember that green is more than just whether the product is certified or not. The key to an effective green disinfectant strategy is to:

✔ Use disinfectants or sanitizers *only* where appropriate.

✔ Use the *right* disinfectant or sanitizer for the job.

✔ Choose the product with the *least* impact on health and the environment.

✔ Use the *correct dilution* and use the product in accordance with the manufacturer's instructions, especially as this applies to dwell time.

Challenge your supplier to help you identify areas and situations where the use of disinfectants or sanitizers is appropriate and to find greener alternatives to traditional choices.

Hand soaps

From a public health perspective, little can compete with a good hand-washing program to reduce or prevent the human-to-human transmission of disease. The hand soap should:

✔ Remove the types of soil encountered where it will be used. That is, a soap intended for use in a garage should have good degreasing capability compared to one intended for use in an office building.

✔ Lather well without requiring excessive application. Consider the newer foaming soaps that deliver equivalent lather with 50 percent less product dispensed.

✔ Not irritate the users' skin.

✔ Have little or no fragrance or dye.

✔ Utilize dispensers that are easily filled. If a soap comes with a replaceable pouch, it should be made of plastic with high recycled content. If the dispenser is refillable, it should be easy to remove for cleaning between refills.

✔ *Not* contain sanitizing or antimicrobial agents except as a preservative in the soap or where specifically required by health code or other regulations, such as in food-preparation areas or acute health care settings.

Why shouldn't hand soaps contain antimicrobial agents? After all, if we're so concerned about human health, why wouldn't we want to use hand sanitizers as much as possible? Well, there's little need to kill the bugs that end up on your hands. A good quality soap removes the harmful organisms and allows you to rinse them down the drain. After they're gone, they're no longer a threat to you or anyone else. Research finds little evidence that health is further protected by using an antimicrobial-containing hand soap compared to good ol' fashioned soap and water.

When you can't wash: Hand sanitizers

A personal hand sanitizer can be ideal for your green program when washing hands with soap and water is inconvenient or impossible, as an additional level of protection, or during flu and cold season. Look for a water-based alternative to the common alcohol-based formulas, which may lead to dry, chapped hands. When an alcohol-based product is spilled or dripped on the floor, it can damage the finish or carpet.

Water-based alternatives are gentle on your skin, nonharmful to floors and equally effective in killing harmful organisms. Furthermore, most hand-sanitizing protocols require the hands to remain wet for 20 seconds for the product to be effective. In the real world, alcohol-based hand sanitizers evaporate in less than the prescribed time period, whereas the water-based products take longer to evaporate, thus increasing contact time and improving the ability to kill the harmful organisms that might be present on hands.

On the other hand, there are very good reasons for *not* overusing antimicrobial hand soaps. In the first place, most are very irritating to skin, causing hands to lose moisture, dry out, and become cracked with extensive use unless additional moisturizers and other ingredients are added to the soap. Like overusing surface disinfectants, overusing antimicrobial hand soaps can lead to the growth of resistant organisms, defeating our ability to kill them when necessary. And finally, the addition of antimicrobial active ingredients can significantly increase the cost of the product with little actual benefit.

Other cleaning chemicals

A variety of other chemicals are used to maintain facilities. Many traditional chemicals such as drain cleaners, furniture and metal polishes, concrete, and other heavy-duty cleaners often have known health and environmental problems associated with them. And although zero risk is a pipe dream (everything has some potential to cause harm), choosing greener alternatives can reduce the potential for harm to occupants, the people using the products, and the environment.

Several traditional cleaners contain hazardous chemicals. Here are a few examples:

✔ Many traditional drain cleaners use concentrated sodium hydroxide (CAS 1310-73-2) and bleach (CAS 7681-52-9). These products are very hazardous and can permanently damage eyes and skin, can be respiratory irritants, and when mixed with other commonly used cleaning products can produce a deadly gas. And yes, people do die from this every year!

✔ Many traditional metal and furniture polishes contain ammonia (CAS 7664-41-7) a respiratory irritant, and petroleum distillates (CAS 8052-41-3), which can be toxic to the nervous system. Additionally, they frequently contain petroleum-based oils, which can have a variety of both health and environmental impacts.

✔ Heavy-duty cleaner/degreasers may contain 2-butoxyethanol (CAS 111-76-2), often referred to as *butyl* and suspected of being a developmental, endocrine, and reproductive toxicant — among other concerns — as it passes through the skin and enters the body. These cleaners also likely contain sodium hydroxide, which raises the pH and can burn eyes and skin.

Many of these ingredients are made from petroleum — a valuable but limited nonrenewable natural resource. Unfortunately, as in the case of disinfectants, no third-party standards exist to help you identify the amount of alternative resources, frequently referred to as *biobased materials,* in these products. Such standards are currently under development.

When selecting your green products, you need to rely upon the basic definition of a green product: reduced health and environmental impacts compared to the more commonly used products. Your strategy should be that if the product has an extreme pH and can burn eyes and skin, you'd select a greener alternative that has a more moderate pH (something closer to 7). If the product is a respiratory irritant or neurotoxicant, you can replace it with something that isn't. If the product is made from nonrenewable natural resources, you can replace it with bacteria-based products or one derived from a rapidly renewable agricultural product.

Finding further resources

Several other organizations provide specific recommendations for choosing green cleaning chemicals. These include:

✔ *The Pennsylvania Guidelines to Environmental Purchasing:* This manual provides a wealth of excellent information about choosing safer products along with use guidelines for janitorial procedures.

✔ *Center for a New American Dream:* The Center is a not-for-profit environmental advocacy group that offers a comprehensive environmentally preferable purchasing program online. Their online database lists purchasing programs from around the country, as well as products approved through those various programs.

✔ *The Healthy Schools Campaign Resource Guide for IAQ:* This excellent action guide is focused on developing indoor air quality improvement programs in schools. Because the chemicals used to clean our schools have a demonstrable impact on the quality of the indoor environment, this guide has some good information that will be helpful as you evaluate cleaning products.

✔ *Green Cleaning Network:* This nonprofit organization is focused on advancing the adoption of green cleaning and establishing collaborations between the various organizations working on the issue.

The following table shows you a few alternatives:

Traditional Product	*Green Alternative*
Drain cleaner	Enzyme-based maintainer
Metal and furniture polish	An emulsion containing natural oils and surfactants
Heavy-duty cleaner/degreaser	Citrus or soy-based solvents, detergent-based cleaners, and enzyme-based cleaners

Consider also the VOC content (Volatile Organic Compounds) when you're looking for products that don't fit into categories certified by organizations such as Green Seal or Environmental Choice. The California Air Resources Board has established specific standards for acceptable VOC levels for a number of product categories.

We can't examine these standards in detail here, but you can find the list at www.green.ca.gov/EPP/building/cleaning.htm.

Looking Into Emerging Technologies

The following are some emerging chemical technologies that you should discuss with your suppliers and consider testing as part of your plan for continual improvement:

- ✔ Biobased products made from rapidly renewable natural ingredients such as those from corn, soy, sugar beets, and citrus fruit.

- ✔ Biomimicry, a concept based on the design of products that imitate the way nature eliminates soils and waste — using bacteria to digest organic materials such as fats, oils, and solvents, for example.

- ✔ Disinfectants and sanitizers made from plant-derived essential oils.

- ✔ Coatings that react with sunlight and kill harmful organisms that may be on the surface.

Chapter 11

Choosing Green Cleaning Equipment

*W*hen it comes to choosing green cleaning chemicals, a lot of the work has been done for you. Health, environmental, and performance standards are in place to help guide you through your selections. Not so with equipment, but that doesn't mean you can't make greener choices in this area as well, and it doesn't mean you have to do all kinds of research to do so.

In this chapter, we run down the points you need to consider when comparing powered equipment. Read on for some general guidelines, broken down into three important categories, to help you make more-informed comparisons.

Budget constraints will likely keep you from replacing all "inappropriate" equipment in your facility in one go-around, but if you take a close look at your baseline situation, you can identify the best opportunities and lay the groundwork for future purchases. The plan may identify individual equipment that needs immediate replacement and a phased replacement plan for others.

Although there are no Green Seal or Environmental Choice standards to aid your search for green cleaning equipment, there is good news. The Carpet & Rug Institute does provide certification programs for vacuums and extraction equipment, but its testing is limited to performance and doesn't identify other green attributes (but at least you'll know the equipment works). You can find more information about the Carpet & Rug Institute in Appendix A. As chemical manufacturers have invested more research and development efforts in creating green products, equipment manufacturers have followed suit. The sophistication of the latest equipment is substantially improved over the offerings of only a few years ago.

Look for scrubbers and carpet-cleaning machines that use less water, often substituting foam for dumping gallons of water on the floor. The foam cleans at least as well, is easier to pick up, and dries much more quickly. The advantages include safer floors, less potential for growth of mold or mildew, less dirt left behind, lower water and chemical consumption, and reduced labor costs (fewer trips to fill and empty water and recovery tanks).

Electric motors and propane engines have become more efficient and safer and equipment is being built to be repaired and to last for several years rather than broken and disposed of after only a year of use. Certainly, there continues to be room for improvement and innovation, but the options for buying green equipment today are very encouraging.

Appropriateness: Matching Tool to Job

To maximize effectiveness, a tool should be appropriate for the job it is to perform. A simple example is a vacuum cleaner: Using a 12-inch, single-motor upright vacuum cleaner to clean a 10,000 square foot auditorium is a losing proposition, no matter how great the cleaning powers of the vacuum. Equally inappropriate is attempting to clean a crowded classroom with a 42-inch wide-area vacuum cleaner.

These may seem to be extreme examples, but they happen every day.

In your analysis of the baseline data (see Chapter 5), you will have identified building layout and flooring surfaces. This information should make choosing equipment sized and designed appropriately for the job much easier. The same analysis should be applied to choosing buffing or burnishing equipment, mop styles and sizes, and every other tool or piece of equipment used in the facility.

Measuring Effectiveness

Ineffective tools do more harm than good by giving the appearance of having cleaned but doing little to remove soils, water, dust, and other contaminants, as well as failing to prevent the reintroduction of more contaminants. Making sure your tools perform as they should is a giant step toward going green.

Vacuum cleaners

In the case of a vacuum cleaner, you need to look at both its ability to capture the soil as well as its ability to retain the dust. An excellent starting point is the Green Label Program developed by the Carpet and Rug Institute. Vacuum cleaners that carry the Green Label have been demonstrated to meet minimum standards in the collection and retention of soils and dust.

Carpet extractors

Examine carpet extractors (both portable and truck mount) for their ability to remove the soiled water from the carpet or upholstery. At a minimum, the carpet should be dry within 24 to 48 hours, which is important for several reasons:

- ✓ **As long as a carpet is wet or damp, it's a safety hazard.** Stepping from a damp carpet to a hard floor creates a potential slip-fall incident.

- ✓ **Wet or damp carpets and upholstery are breeding grounds for bacteria, mold, and fungi.** The faster the fabric dries, the less opportunity there is for substantial growth.

- ✓ **Any moisture left in the fabric (more moisture equals longer dry times) is by definition dirty.** The soils were emulsified and suspended in the water. If the water isn't removed, neither is that soil. Therefore, the longer a fabric takes to dry, the dirtier the carpet is.

Automatic scrubbers

Automatic scrubbers should be designed to minimize the amount of water used in the cleaning process (along with the amount of chemical required) and maximize the amount of water recovered. This may be accomplished with new technologies that use foam and/or microfiber pads, which reduce both water and chemical consumption. In addition, effective squeegee design and maintenance helps recover more water and prevent "trails" of soiled solution that need to be captured and removed with a hand mop. This helps avoid potential slip-fall incidents, as well as improve productivity.

Buffing and burnishing equipment

Buffing or burnishing equipment should include active vacuum attachments to capture the dust created during burnishing and prevent it from being inhaled.

Burnishing is an abrasive process, like sanding a piece of wood to make it smoother. It creates a tremendous amount of dust. Capturing this dust has the added benefit of reducing the amount of dust in the air, which can improve cleaning productivity by reducing dusting and other efforts to capture the dust.

 Look for ways to reduce the need for burnishing to improve indoor air quality and reduce labor. Choose floor finishes that don't require burnishing, develop ongoing maintenance programs, and use entry matting programs that reduce floor-care requirements.

Other equipment

Equipment manufacturers continue to increase their research and development spending to develop greener equipment. Some of the new developments include:

- **Self-contained cleaning equipment** that includes both a high-pressure washer with a wet/dry vacuum to make cleaning in bathrooms faster and more efficient, and often reduces chemicals as well.

- **Vapor cleaning devices** may be a good alternative to chemical cleaners such as those that use chlorine for removing mold and mildew. These tools have other applications, including the removal of floor finish to reduce the use of floor-stripping compounds, which are very hazardous cleaning chemicals. These are especially useful on baseboards.

Evaluating Usability

No matter how well a piece of equipment performs its job, if it's uncomfortable, hard to understand how to use, or constantly breaks down, no one will use it. The most powerful vacuum cleaner in the world won't clean a thing if it stays in the closet.

When looking at usability, you want to consider ergonomics, ease of use, training required (and available), durability, and reparability of the equipment. Having to replace old, broken, or inappropriate equipment has huge environmental impacts, not to mention the impact on finances.

Just as equipment should be sized for the task to be performed, size is important to the user as well. Consider the typical custodians in your facility, and purchase new equipment with their capabilities in mind.

Consider these points:

- ✔ **Ease of operation:** Is the equipment difficult to operate or maneuver? Don't be misled by marketing puffery and productivity claims. Assign a team member to actually try the equipment you're considering. Use it in circumstances similar to those in your facility to gauge potential issues and productivity.

- ✔ **Understandability:** Can an average user figure out how to use the equipment with minimal instruction? How about a non-English-speaking user? Are the labels clear; do they use icons or colors as cues? Is there a panic switch to protect the user or passers by?

- ✔ **Training requirements:** What sorts of training materials are required and available for the equipment? Is it icon or color-code based and available in languages other than English?

- ✔ **Dependability and durability:** What is the service record for this equipment? How long has it held up in situations similar to that found in your facility? If it is a new piece of equipment or design, what is the company's track record with their other equipment? Are parts and service readily available? What is the warranty?

Chapter 12

Choosing Green Janitorial Paper Products

. . . .

In This Chapter

▶ Grasping "recycled content"

▶ Finding alternatives to bleaching

▶ Looking at the impact of dispensers

▶ Glimpsing future developments

. . . .

*J*ust try to get through a day without touching paper — we dare you. The amount of paper products a person uses each day is astounding, and a good portion of that is in the form of *janitorial paper products* — toilet paper, paper towels, and so on. In fact, more than 25 million trees are cut down to create janitorial paper in the United States every year! Using green paper takes a heckuva burden off the environment, and doesn't add a financial burden now that most janitorial paper products that have recycled content are priced competitively with virgin paper products.

At present, most janitorial paper products have no recycled content. By requesting and using recycled paper, you help create the demand that builds capacity in the paper industry (they'll make it if people request it). Using paper with recycled content significantly helps protect the environment, and our health depends on a healthy environment.

In this chapter, we take a look at what you need to know to purchase the greenest, healthiest janitorial paper products.

Demystifying 'Recycled Content'

Understanding recycled content — which in the case of paper means material that doesn't come directly from virgin tree pulp — is a little more complicated than you might think. It breaks down as follows on the labels of the products you buy:

✔ **Total recycled content** refers to all recycled materials regardless of where they come from. It might include manufacturing scraps and waste. It's distinguished from post-consumer waste in that it never leaves the factory before being reused.

✔ **Post-consumer content** is the material that was collected after products were purchased, used, and discarded. When you toss out a newspaper, it becomes post-consumer waste.

Post-consumer is a designation that was specifically established by the Environmental Protection Agency to encourage the development of curbside household recycling. The challenge was getting more than 100 million homes (which can be looked at as 100 million small generators of waste) to recycle their materials, as opposed to sending them to the landfill or burning them.

Post-consumer recycling is a challenge because not only do consumers have to be educated to recycle, the infrastructure to collect and process recyclables cost effectively has to be built.

Pre-consumer recycling is waste that's collected straight from a factory — for example, magazines collected from a printer who has made too many copies. This kind of waste is easier to find, separate, and manage. It's easy to get in large quantities, cheaper to sort, and easier to sell.

The Environmental Protection Agency encourages the use of post-consumer products to help build enough participation of homeowners to generate enough volume to make the curbside pickup system cost-effective. Thus, we can help enormously by purchasing products specifically made with post-consumer content and by educating occupants about the importance of recycling and to help the recycling efforts in our buildings succeed.

Furthermore, federal agencies are required by law (Resources Conservation and Recovery Act, Section 6002) to buy recycled products with post-consumer content. This requirement is part of what's called the Comprehensive Procurement Guidelines (CPG).

Until the industry can reach 100 percent post-consumer recycled content, the CPG calls for the following:

Material	PCR content
Toilet Tissue	20% to 60%
Facial Tissue	10% to 15%
Hand Towels	40% to 60%
Industrial Wipes	At least 40%

For more information about the EPA Comprehensive Procurement Guidelines, please visit www.epa.gov/epaoswer/non-hw/procure/products/tissue.htm.

Quality among these products varies. Simply because a product has a high amount of post-consumer or total recycled content does *not* mean that the product is of poor quality. You can find many very good products with a large amount of post-consumer recycled content. As with any other product, you need to evaluate the options in your facility.

The Downside of Bleaching

Most paper is bleached to make it perfectly white. The traditional bleaching process uses elemental chlorine or chlorine dioxide. When chlorine enters the environment where it mixes with other naturally occurring organic material in the waste stream it can produce dioxins and furans, which are some of the most deadly chemicals on the face of the earth (they cause cancer and developmental problems in humans, and they're *persistent in the environment* — that is, they don't go away).

Furthermore, one of the major production methods of chlorine requires the use of mercury cells, which release mercury, a heavy metal and known neurotoxin and developmental toxin into the environment.

In recent years, many paper mills have invested tens of millions of dollars to eliminate elemental chlorine originally used in their bleaching process and replace it with chlorine dioxide. This process is known as *elemental chlorine free* or ECF. It doesn't eliminate completely the use of chlorine, but chlorine dioxide reduces the amount of harmful byproducts by more than 90 percent and is a superior green alternative to traditional paper bleached with elemental chlorine.

Other paper mills have gone one step further and use nonchlorinated methods such as hydrogen peroxide for bleaching. This bleaching process even further reduces the inadvertent production of dioxins and is known as *process chlorine free* or PCF.

Although most of the programs that have served as the roadmap for product standards in this chapter require the use of paper products with a high amount of post-consumer recycled content fiber, these same programs typically identify the issues associated with bleaching and encourage or prefer the use of process chlorine free (PCF) products but don't require it.

Janitorial paper is a high-touch item. Choosing the best paper products for your facility begins with identifying candidates from those that meet the minimum CPG standards, Green Seal standards GS-01 and GS09 Environmental Choice standards CCD-082 and CCD-086, and those endorsed by the CFPA. These candidates should then be evaluated by your team for cost, availability, and acceptance by the building occupants.

Dispensers Make a Difference

The style of paper towel and type of dispenser can have a significant impact on paper usage, waste, health, and costs:

✔ Hands-free paper hand towel dispensers that eliminate cranks and levers cut down on the germs that are passed from person to person and improve the protection of occupant health. *Note:* You don't have to change to the battery-operated or electric dispensers that deliver a towel when your hand is waved in front of an electric eye. Although these can be effective and attractive dispensers, the simple version that leaves some exposed paper to be pulled is equally effective in protecting against the transmission of germs and eliminates batteries and motors along with the environmental impacts associated with the production of energy and all the other components.

✔ Large rolls of toilet paper reduce packaging waste, are typically cheaper than many smaller rolls, and reduce the labor needed to change the rolls. This cuts down on costs and complaints from toilet-tissue dispensers being empty. It also eliminates the waste from replacing small rolls that might otherwise run out before the custodians plan to return to service the restroom.

✔ Replacing C-fold and multifold towel dispensers with roll towel products and hands-free dispensers not only eliminates waste, but saves money and labor to restock the dispensers. (People tend to pull out — and thereby waste — more C-fold towels than they need.)

Make sure that when you consider the benefits, you also consider the costs for changing dispensers. Your paper supplier or distributor will often help defray these costs when you commit to a longer-term contract.

What about electric, hot-air hand dryers? There are environmental benefits to be had by switching to energy-efficient electric hand dryers, which don't use tree fiber, reduce environmental impacts from manufacturing, and virtually eliminate waste.

But our personal bias comes from a health standpoint. From a public health perspective, nothing is more important than hand washing. Thus, things that encourage hand washing are preferable to those that discourage hand washing. After 25 years in the cleaning industry, our experience has been that people prefer paper when both are available. So, if an electric dryer discourages people from washing their hands, it's not a good thing — even if the number of people discouraged is small.

We're also concerned about what happens to the water from people's hands. The typical procedure for using an electric dryer is to shake the excess water from our hands. But where does that water go? If the excess water is being flicked onto floors it can lead to slips and falls. And on both floors and walls it can contribute to mold and other problems.

When high-velocity air blows the water droplets off hands, where do those droplets go? And perhaps more importantly, what are those droplets potentially contaminated with? An airborne particle potentially contaminated with pathogenic organisms doesn't seem like a good option, especially when another option is so readily available. Thus our preference for paper.

Eying Emerging Technologies

The following are some emerging paper technologies that you should discuss with your suppliers and consider testing as part of the plan for continual improvement:

✔ **Products made from trees that are rapidly renewable:** Most trees can take 20 to 50 or more years before they grow to maturity. Other trees, such as Eucalyptus, mature in only 10 years, which meets the definition of a rapidly renewable natural resource.

✔ **Products made from alternative fibers:** We have become accustomed to thinking of janitorial paper as coming from tree fiber. But why? Paper can be made from any source of fiber. Alternative fiber sources such as those made from reed or agricultural waste may be new alternatives to be considered.

✔ **Products made from sustainable harvest forests:** Most forestry operations are very conscientious, but some are not. *Clear cutting* of forests, where literally every tree regardless of type, age, health, and so on, is cut down is the most efficient and cheapest method for harvesting fiber, but it's also the most destructive to the ecosystem. Sustainable forestry practices are much more selective about which trees are removed in an effort to manage the long-term health of the forest. Although it's still difficult to identify how the forest was managed, sustainable forestry is becoming a bigger issue and in the future may become a differentiator when buying janitorial products as well.

Chapter 13

Choosing Entryway Matting

● ●

In This Chapter

▶ Understanding how big is big enough

▶ Placing mats for optimal effectiveness

▶ Getting a grip on mat quality

▶ Working with a salesperson

● ●

*G*reen cleaning starts at the door, with high-quality floor mats. When you place the right mat in the right spot, you're installing one of the best pollution-prevention strategies available. Here's why:

✔ Up to 80 percent of the soil in a building is tracked in on the feet of people entering.

✔ Up to 24 pounds of dirt can be tracked in by just 1,000 people coming through an entrance during a 20-day work period.

✔ The cost to remove just one pound of dirt after it's tracked throughout a building can exceed $500.

✔ As much as 42 percent of the floor finish can be damaged or removed after 1,500 people have walked within the first 6 feet of an entrance without a matting system, which results in poorer initial impressions of a building, increased cleaning costs, and a greater possibility for slips and falls to occur. Slips, trips, and falls are the leading cause of occupational accidents and result in more than 300,000 disabling injuries each year.

If you can reduce the amount of soil coming in, you have enormous opportunities to reduce the potential adverse impact on the health and performance of building occupants, reduce the frequency of stripping and refinishing floors, reduce damage to carpets and delicate electronic equipment, and improve the overall appearance of your facility.

Looking beyond cost savings

Matting systems reduce the amount of cleaning a building requires. That may sound great, but we focus on the *other* benefits of matting systems in this chapter because we firmly believe that currently most buildings aren't cleaned enough. Any labor savings resulting from green or other traditional strategies should be redirected to create healthier, higher-performing buildings, especially for those occupants who are sensitive or vulnerable. The misguided strategy of solely focusing on cost reduction is harming not only building occupants but your ability to manage, protect, and market the building.

Health and cleaning benefits aside, you probably want mats to look nice, and certainly you can get good looks along with functionality. Mats are available in all kinds of colors and designs. You can even buy a custom-printed mat with a business logo.

Mat Size Counts

For something that sits underfoot and is overlooked by just about everyone who walks across it, a mat serves several important purposes, but only if it has been chosen properly.

One of the biggest problems with most existing entryway matting programs is that they're simply too small. We frequently tell facility managers that if they're using small 3-x-5 foot entry mats, they should stop pretending and save their money. These mats are simply too small to be effective.

An entry mat needs to be long enough for each foot to hit the mat at least two times. That means the mat must be at least 10 to 15 feet long. Studies show that 30 feet of a high-quality, well-placed entry matting system covering both immediately outside as well as inside the entry can remove nearly 100 percent of dirt, sand, and moisture! And less dirt, sand, and moisture results in all kinds of good stuff.

Granted, we've been in plenty of buildings where there simply wasn't enough space to install a 10- to 15-foot entry mat, much less 30 feet of matting. But we hope that after reading this chapter, you reevaluate your entryway mats and consider how you can increase the size of the mats in your building.

Putting Mats Where They Matter Most

Far too many buildings use entryway matting systems only at the main public entrance. These mats can be decorative and effective, and we're glad they're used. But although visitors may typically enter only through the main doors, occupants and vendors often use other doors. Thus, it might be very valuable for you to do a quick audit — walk the perimeter of the building and evaluate which other doors are actually used and thus could benefit from entrance matting systems. Don't forget the entrances from any parking structures and underground garages.

When you audit a building to determine how to allocate mats, remember the following:

- ✔ **Take pictures of the entryway to show the matting system or the lack thereof.** This is a terrific way to document the location, that current matting systems are too small or inappropriate, and the fact that people use the various entrances.

- ✔ **Conduct your audit during a busy part of the day when foot traffic is highest.** We dream about buildings where all of our recommendations are immediately acted upon, but often resources are limited and prioritizing necessary. Auditing the building during a busy part of the day helps identify the volume of foot traffic at each door and allows you to prioritize matting requirements based on volume and need.

- ✔ **Check the entries at different times of year.** If the seasons bring dramatic changes to the area, you may need to repeat your audit at different times of the year to ensure that the entry matting systems are appropriate for changes in weather conditions. Check again in the winter, for example, to address the impacts of snow and ice removal.

One of the most overlooked opportunities to use entryway matting systems is inside a building where occupants enter through a parking garage, especially when the parking garage is underground. These entrances often have high levels of soils that are tracked directly into the building and would benefit from a high-quality and appropriately sized mat.

For the most-effective system, place high-quality and appropriately sized mats *outside* the doors. We do recognize that in many locations, placing entryway mats outside the front door isn't practical, such as in front of a commercial building that opens to a busy downtown sidewalk. But do us a favor and think about it anyway. You might find some locations where it would work just fine and truly make a difference.

Outside mats are especially valuable in areas that get a lot of rain and snow, or where the landscapers have used a lot of flowering and berry-producing plants.

Outdoor mats are different from indoor mats and are typically designed to scrape mud and gross soils from shoes. These mats also are designed to allow water, snow, and so on, to either pass through the mat or be channeled in a way that keeps the surface of the mat relatively dry. After they become wet or get loaded with soils, far too many mats serve no value and can actually contribute to the soils being tracked into the building.

Determining Quality

Just as a too-small mat won't bring the desired effect, one that's of poor quality thwarts your dirt-banishing and health-improving efforts. Size is more easily quantifiable, but quality mats do have a few common characteristics.

A glimpse of future mats

When we look at the carpet industry, we see some possible clues about where the entryway matting business may be headed. Keep your eyes out for these and perhaps you can be the first one to bring these innovations to your building.

Some of those innovations include products made with recycled content. Other innovations include products constructed with innovative new fibers made from a starch called polylactic acid (PLA) — a rapidly renewable natural resource made from corn rather than vinyl, rubber, or other petroleum derivatives.

Others are looking for alternatives to mats made with polyvinyl chloride (PVC), because there's some concern that the basic building block of PVC, vinyl chloride, is carcinogenic and that if it's inadvertently burned in a building or landfill fire, it creates dioxin, another carcinogen. The most readily available alternative to PVC mats are those made from rubber.

Companies will instate "take-back" programs where you return used mats to the manufacturer, who makes them into new mats — as opposed to sending them to landfills.

As awareness of and demand for green mats and carpets grow, so too will the innovations.

When you're buying mats, consider the following:

- **Weight:** If a mat is too light, it won't stay in place and may therefore contribute to slip-and-fall accidents. Some light-weight mats may curl up at the edges and corners, which also can lead to slips, trips, and falls.

- **Construction:** Effective mats use bi-level construction that resembles hard ridges. The ridges create channels for soils and moisture to accumulate. This significantly increases what the mat can hold and reduces what gets tracked into the building.

Planning Your Purchase

When buying mats, don't just look for the lowest price. Your best bet is to buy from a salesperson who can truly help you understand what it takes to develop a comprehensive entryway matting system. Here are a few things to keep in mind when working with a salesperson:

- Ask him to explain his product (which may include one line of mats or several different options), and ask whether he can do an audit of your entrances.

- Ask the salesperson to provide some ideas that will help you justify the investment in more, bigger, longer, and/or higher-quality mats.

- Ask whether the company will provide a cleaning strategy for the entrance, the matting systems, and the exterior of the building. It takes all three to really be effective.

Chapter 14

Choosing Additional Green Cleaning Tools and Supplies

● ●

In This Chapter

▶ Keeping green on the brain while shopping

▶ Making the most of magical microfiber

● ●

*Y*our green cleaning toolkit will take some time to complete. As you continue to add the tools and supplies you need, look for the greenest alternatives. In this chapter, we give you a few tips for making green choices.

Shopping Green

Green cleaning means that health — of the environment and of the people who use the building you're cleaning — is your primary concern. The following points keep health and the environment at the forefront in various ways:

✔ **Look for recycled content.** Plastic shows up in mop and broom handles, buckets and wringers, scrapers, plungers, Johnny brushes, and so on. Ask suppliers for options that are made with significant amounts of recycled content, and when possible specify post-consumer content. (To better understand the difference between post- and preconsumer waste, check out Chapter 12.)

✔ **Consider ergonomics.** Choosing mop handles and other tools that fit the person using them and looking for those that have ergonomic designs will help prevent injuries and enhance your employees' comfort and productivity. Consider replacing your dust mops and wet mops with microfiber mops. They're lighter and easier to use. Imagine what a 32-ounce mop feels like saturated with water after a 4-hour shift. A microfiber mop weighs a fraction of that, and it works better!

One of the easiest ways to evaluate the ergonomic features of various tools is to ask your supplier to provide test or evaluation samples of various alternatives. Allowing your staff to try these products for several shifts will help quickly identify those that make the job easier versus those that don't!

✔ **Insist on durable tools and supplies.** If you're using mop buckets, dollies, carts, and so on that need to be replaced every year, consider a plan to replace them with more durable alternatives. Doing so significantly reduces the impact on landfills and on the environment by eliminating the impacts from all the raw materials, energy, and other things that go into making the new replacement products.

Take some time to look at how the competing products are constructed: Are parts welded or bolted together or simply press-fitted? Do wheels turn easily or do they tend to bind and stick? Well-made items, designed to perform for longer periods of time, usually work better right out of the box.

Make sure your distributor or supplier understands that you're looking for longer-lasting products and that your relationship with that supplier depends on her ability to meet your needs. Professional salespeople recognize that developing a long-term relationship with a savvy buyer is very profitable. They will work to earn and maintain your trust.

✔ **Find tools that replace chemicals.** Before turning to a chemical, take a look at your options. Challenge your supplier to demonstrate tools offered by his company that replace or reduce the need for using chemicals. You may find an alternative such as:

- Using a plumber's snake rather than a caustic drain opener. Doing so is safer for the user and building occupants and potentially less damaging to the facility itself.

- Dusting with microfiber cloths that require no added chemicals such as dusting sprays.

- Removing hard water and other stains from the inside of toilet fixtures with a pumice stick, replacing acids and other dangerous chemicals.

Choose tools that trap and remove dirt rather than spreading it around. In other words, get rid of the wool or feather duster!

The Magic of Microfiber

Microfiber, an extremely thin fiber made from polyester or nylon, is an excellent tool for green cleaning. It can be made from recycled content, offers significant ergonomic advantages, reduces or replaces the need for chemicals, and traps and removes soil versus spreading it around.

Microfiber comes in hard or soft weaves, sometimes blended with cotton, and therefore is appropriate in a variety of different cleaning situations. Cloths made from soft fibers are ideal for dusting, polishing, and general cleaning for any surface. When blended with cotton, the cloth becomes useful for damp or wet cleaning, ideal for restrooms, break areas, or kitchens. Finally, when the fibers are split in the manufacturing process to create sharp edges, the fibers are said to be hard. These are useful for cleaning glass and other hard, nonscratchable surfaces.

Some common uses for microfiber cloths include:

- **Dusting:** Soft fiber cloths are ideal dusting tools. These require no spray polish or other chemical, yet they effectively trap and remove up to 99 percent of the soils. With a little elbow grease, you can use them to remove smudges and coffee rings from typical office furniture.

- **Glass cleaning:** Blends of hard and soft fibers result in a cloth that is very effective at cleaning scratch-resistant surfaces with little water and no chemicals. These cloths make excellent tools for dry-cleaning mirrors and door glass.

- **Wet cleaning:** Fiber cloths that are woven and blended with a small amount of cotton or other water-holding material allow for an excellent wet-cleaning cloth. These are ideal in kitchens and restrooms. Requiring minimal or no chemicals, these cloths clean, polish, and rinse clean for re-use.

- **Dust mopping:** Used dry, microfiber mops are good replacements for the traditional dust mop. They require no treatment and will collect more dust than any treated dust mop.

- **Wet mopping:** The same mop used damp can effectively clean lightly soiled hard floors. This is an ideal tool for break areas and small tile sections in buildings that are primarily carpet.

  Spraying a diluted general purpose cleaner on this mop makes it a good replacement for the traditional damp mop. Not only is it easier to use than a heavy wet mop, the user can leave the bucket and wringer in the closet!

✔ **Floor finishing:** Specially designed and woven microfiber flat mops are better for applying floor finish than traditional rayon finish mops. They're lighter (reducing fatigue and the mistakes that often result), and they also lay a virtually perfect thin coat of finish.

✔ **Scrubbing:** Some manufacturers now offer microfiber floor pads for scrubbers. David, one of the authors, designed a microfiber floor pad several years ago. Testing demonstrated it to be more effective on hard floors and carpet than traditional abrasive pads or bonnets. Using a fraction of the water and chemicals, these pads cleaned more effectively and left a higher shine on vinyl composite tile (VCT) floors (measured with a gloss meter) than traditional cleaning methods.

Microfiber offers some fantastic benefits, but it isn't perfect. You need to launder your cloths between uses, and they're more expensive (per cloth) than typical janitorial wipes. However, when you look at the "all-in" cost — cost of purchase, number of launderings, how long between replacement, as well as savings in chemicals and labor — microfiber can prove to be one of the best bargains out there!

Consider buying different colored microfiber cloths so that the color-coding can help the custodians separate the cloths used for dry dusting from those used for cleaning toilets and other contaminated surfaces and from those used for cleaning surfaces that occupants frequently touch.

Part IV
The Part of Tens

The 5th Wave   By Rich Tennant

"They're moving on to Chapter 2. That should daze and confuse them enough for us to finish changing the tire and get the heck out of here."

In this part . . .

This part gives you a great way to quickly gain some wisdom about green cleaning. We discuss risks associated with poor indoor air and ten guidelines for green cleaning.

Chapter 15

Ten Risks Associated with Poor Indoor Air Quality

• •

*1*n recent years, asthma rates in school children and adults have increased alarmingly. Cancer rates are rising, work-related illnesses and allergies continue to climb, and reports of sick buildings are at record levels. These facts aren't the fault of cleaning products or procedures. However, the increases clearly are related to the indoor environment. After all, people spend 80 to 90 percent of their time indoors, and the EPA estimates that typical indoor air may be two to five times as polluted as the outdoor air.

Although cleaning may not be the *cause,* a different way of cleaning may be part of the *solution.* In this chapter, we show you some of the risks associated with poor indoor air quality.

Allergies

A major concern associated with exposure to biological pollutants is allergic reactions, which range from rhinitis, nasal congestion, inflammation of the eyes, and hives to asthma. Notable triggers for these diseases are allergens derived from dust mites; other pests, including cockroaches; pets (cats, dogs, birds, rodents); molds; and protein-containing furnishings, including feathers, kapok, and so on. In occupational settings, more unusual allergens (for example, bacterial enzymes, algae) have caused asthma epidemics. Probably most proteins of nonhuman origin can cause asthma in some of your building's occupants.

The most significant activities you can undertake to reduce the impact of allergic reactions include:

✔ Identify vulnerable groups and take special precautions in these areas including increased cleaning intensity and frequency, scheduling any cleaning activities for when these people are away from the area, and frequently evaluating potential impacts.

✓ Ensure your vacuum cleaners effectively remove and retain microscopic particles (down to 0.5 microns or better). Change the bag or empty the collection bin after each shift.

✓ Use microfiber cloths and mops for dusting and dust mopping.

✓ Minimize or eliminate the use of aerosol-propelled cleaning products.

Asthma

Reaching epidemic levels in the United States in recent years, asthma affects people of all ages and races. Most common in children, asthma has resulted in more than 14 million missed school days in the past several years. Adult onset asthma related to working conditions is increasing at significant rates. Asthma is a chronic disease characterized by inflammation of the airways. During an asthma episode, the airways in the lungs narrow, making breathing difficult.

Asthma episodes may be triggered by a variety of indoor and outdoor pollutants and contaminants. Some of the most common indoor irritants include:

✓ Animal dander

✓ Cockroaches and other pests

✓ Mold

✓ Secondhand smoke

✓ Dust mites

✓ Automobile exhaust

Vacuum cleaners that effectively collect and *retain* microscopic dust particles are a key part of the solution. Microfiber cloths for dusting and dust mopping help collect microscopic particles rather than moving them about or "kicking" them back into the air to be breathed.

Infectious Diseases

Infectious diseases are by definition carried from person to person. Although certain diseases can be transmitted by contact with animals as well, ultimately it is the contact between people that concerns you most inside your building.

Clearly, by focusing your cleaning efforts on improving health (versus cleaning solely for appearance) you are in a much better position to reduce the spread of infectious diseases.

One of the single most important steps is to simply do a better job of hand washing. Although about 70 percent of people *report* that they wash their hands after using the restroom, only about 60 percent actually do. Make it easy for building occupants to wash their hands. Install foaming soap dispensers; they're less messy, require less water, and make effective hand washing quick and easy.

Other things to consider:

✔ Install touch-free dispensers and fixtures in restrooms.

✔ Use photo cells to turn lights on and off (eliminating a touch point).

✔ Give all building occupants a microfiber cloth to wipe their keyboards and phones.

✔ Ensure your procedures call for cleaning touch points on a regular basis.

✔ Avoid overusing disinfectants (see Chapter 10).

✔ Check janitors' closets to ensure used mops, rags, and other reusable supplies are properly laundered and stored.

Increased Absenteeism

Whether caused by asthma, allergies, disease, or general discomfort related to contaminants in the indoor environment, absenteeism significantly reduces productivity and costs our economy billions of dollars every year.

Again, refocusing your cleaning efforts to improving health and the quality of the indoor environment versus appearance will have an impact on the building occupants' comfort and well-being. Studies have repeatedly demonstrated improvements in attendance (both in schools and in office environments) when steps are taken to improve indoor environmental quality.

Learning Problems

Various chemicals have been linked to developmental damage in children, which would certainly have impact on learning. It is beyond the scope of this book to address those types of issues, although it should be noted that green cleaning seeks to minimize impacts on the environment and how children and others are exposed to contaminants in the environment.

However, learning is also impacted by a child's health and everyone has certainly seen how cleaning can impact that. Sick children, even if they're not absent from school, simply can't learn as well as if they were healthy.

Removing irritants and contaminants from their environment will help children with allergies and asthma avoid the episodes that prevent effective learning. Chemicals that minimize impacts on human health can help avoid triggering episodes and are much safer to use in these environments.

And it's not just "at-risk" children that are impacted by exposure to chemicals or poor cleaning practices. The "normal" child can be hurt if exposed to many typical chemicals, and will begin to feel debilitated when exposed to irritants and contaminants for hours, days, and weeks at a time.

When a school goes through an environmental "makeover" the performance of all students tends to increase, not just the poor performers or at-risk students.

Sinusitis

Sinusitis refers to inflamed or infected sinuses. This definition understates the pain this condition can cause. Sinusitis is typically broken into three types: *acute* (lasting less than four weeks), *subacute* (lasting four to six weeks), and *chronic* (which lasts more than eight weeks). Recurrent sinusitis describes several acute attacks occurring within a year.

More than 37 million Americans are struck by sinusitis every year and at least 32 million chronic cases are reported to the Centers for Disease Control each year. Health care costs related to sinusitis are estimated to be $5.8 million annually.

The causes of sinusitis are varied. Some researchers say that it is an infectious disease while others argue that it isn't. All agree that people with reduced immune system functionality (ranging from those with diabetes, allergies, asthma, AIDS, to a common cold) are at greater risk to developing sinusitis. Some of the causes of sinusitis that these people are most susceptible to include certain types of molds and fungi, bacteria, and various air pollutants such as cigarette smoke.

Cleaning programs should attempt to identify vulnerable populations within the building and take steps to ensure you reduce the contaminants and irritants in these areas as much as possible. Cleaning activities that tend to raise dust levels (vacuuming, dusting, buffing, or burnishing floors for example) should be scheduled for when these people are away from the area and sufficient time allowed after cleaning for the dust to settle before they return.

Sick Building Syndrome

The term *Sick Building Syndrome* (SBS) describes situations in which building occupants experience acute health and comfort effects that appear to be linked to time spent in a building, but no specific illness or cause can be identified. The complaints may be localized in a particular room or zone, or may be widespread throughout the building.

Some indications of SBS can include:

✔ Occupants complain of problems such as headaches, eye, nose, or throat irritations, dry or itchy skin, dizziness, dry cough, difficulty in concentrating, fatigue, and sensitivity to odors.

✔ Occupants (or their doctors) are unable to identify the cause of the problems.

✔ Most of the occupants report they feel better soon after leaving the building.

It is important to note that these complaints may be the result of other causes including illnesses contracted outside the building, acute sensitivity (for instance allergies), job-related stress, and other factors. However, studies show that these symptoms may be caused or exacerbated by indoor air-quality problems.

Solutions to Sick Building Syndrome usually include combinations of the following:

✔ **Pollutant source removal or modification**. Some examples include routine maintenance of HVAC systems, replacement of water-stained ceiling tile and water-damaged floor tile or carpeting, venting contaminant source emissions to the outdoors (chemical storage areas, print shops, copy rooms, mechanical and wood shop areas), and storage and use of paints, adhesives, solvents, and pesticides in well-ventilated areas.

✔ **Increasing ventilation rates** and air distribution often can be a cost-effective means of reducing indoor pollutant levels.

✔ **Education and communication** are important elements in both remedial and preventive indoor air-quality management programs. When building occupants, management, and maintenance personnel fully understand the causes and consequences of indoor air-quality problems, they can work more effectively together to prevent problems from occurring, or to solve them if they do.

Building Related Illnesses

Building Related Illnesses are diagnosable illnesses that can be attributed directly to the building. Building Related Illness (BRI) is different than Sick Building Syndrome in the ability to identify both the illness and the cause.

Some indications of BRI can include:

- Occupants complain of problems such as cough, chest tightness, fever, chills, and muscle aches.

- The problems can be clinically defined and have clearly identifiable causes.

- Occupants may require significant recovery times after leaving the building.

If one or more of the occupants of your building have been diagnosed with a BRI, your green cleaning plan should be modified to include the procedures designed to alleviate the problem that was identified. In some cases, the issue is not cleaning, but may be related to the air-handling system or even outside pollutants being brought into the building. For example a parking garage may be situated in a way that causes exhaust fumes to be forced into an air intake.

In general, following the recommendations outlined in this book as you develop a green cleaning plan, respecting the needs of vulnerable populations, and ensuring that the procedures are properly followed will help prevent or alleviate any BRI issues in your facility.

Low Productivity and Poor Performance

Low productivity and poor performance are the results of a Building Related Illness or Sick Building Syndrome. Just as sick children can't learn as effectively as healthy children, employees that are suffering from allergies, asthma, and other BRI can't possibly perform at the level of healthier employees.

The cost of reduced productivity and performance arising from illnesses or fatigue (caused by poor indoor environment) is staggering. Recent studies indicate it exceeds $60 billion annually in the United States. Just a small improvement in productivity could more than pay for any additional costs associated with a green cleaning program.

Chapter 16

Ten Guidelines for Green Cleaning

Caring for a commercial or institutional facility is a huge task. Developing and implementing a green cleaning program that effectively protects occupants' health, while minimizing cleaning's impact on the environment is equally significant.

Whether you're explaining your green cleaning plan to a new employee, a vendor, or someone in senior management, you need to capture the most significant aspects. This chapter highlights the key points of a well-designed green cleaning program.

Put Health and the Environment First

A green cleaning program protects health and the environment first, appearance second. Even buildings that appear clean can be extremely unhealthy. But the inverse is rarely true: When a building is cleaned in a way that ensures the health of the occupants, it usually looks clean and snazzy.

Stop Dirt at the Door

Paying attention to entryways — inside and out — helps keep dirt from getting into a building in the first place. A significant amount of the dirt, dust, and other pollutants come into your building on people's feet. Install walk-off mats, which will help to trap and remove dirt before it enters the building. Consult your mat supplier to choose the proper style for outside and inside each entryway. Proper and frequent cleaning of the mats is critical if you want them to keep grabbing dirt before it gets in.

Target Spray Cleaners

Minimize airborne chemicals by replacing aerosols with trigger sprayers and setting them for a coarse spray pattern. Spray the cleaning cloth rather than the surface to be cleaned. Consider using microfiber cloths to reduce or eliminate the need for general-purpose cleaners.

Banish Dust

Capture dust and microscopic particles rather than putting them back into the air. Replace traditional dust mops with microfiber dust mops or use vacuum cleaners to dry-clean hard floors. Use high-efficiency vacuum cleaners and vacuum cleaner filters and bags. Use microfiber cloths to capture dust rather than rags and furniture polish.

Touch Up Touchpoints

Focus on touchpoints, those spots where people come into contact with the facility's fixtures. Door handles, push bars, light switches, public phones, elevator buttons, and so on are prime points for disease transmission.

Disinfect without Overdoing It

Choose and apply disinfectants properly. Resist the temptation to overuse disinfectants. Good basic cleaning procedures are as effective as disinfectants for cleaning most surfaces. Follow the manufacturer's instructions for precleaning, dilution, and dwell time when using disinfectants.

EPA Design for the Environment Program

We discuss the EPA Design for the Environment (www.epa.gov/dfe) program in Chapter 10. Contact it at Design for the Environment (DfE), Office of Pollution Prevention & Toxics, US EPA, 1200 Pennsylvania Ave., NW, Mail Code 7406-M, Washington, DC, 20460.

Environmental Choice

We discuss the Environmental Choice (www.environmental choice.com) program in depth in Chapter 10. Contact it at Environmental Choice Program, c/o TerraChoice Environmental Marketing, 1280 Old Innes Suite 801, Ottawa, Ontario K1B 5M7, Canada. Phone: 800-478-0399.

Greenguard Environmental Institute

We discuss the Greenguard Environmental Institute (www. greenguard.org) in Chapter 10. Contact it at Greenguard Environmental Institute, 1341 Capital Circle, Suite A, Atlanta, Georgia 30067. Phone: 800-427-9681.

Green Seal

We discuss the Green Seal (www.greenseal.org) program in depth in Chapter 10. Contact it at 1001 Connecticut Ave., NW, Suite 827, Washington, DC 20036. Phone: 202-872-6400.

ISSA Cleaning Industry Management Standard

ISSA (www.issa.com/standard) is the leading trade association representing the commercial and institutional cleaning industry. Its Cleaning Industry Management Standard (CIMS) is a management framework designed to assist building service contractors and in-house service providers develop quality, customer-centered organizations, and based on those universally accepted principles that have proven to be the hallmarks of well-managed, successful cleaning operations. Contact it at 7373 N. Lincoln Ave., Lincolnwood, Illinois. Phone: 800-225-4772.

United States Green Building Council (USGBC)

The USGBC (www.usgbc.org) developed the Leadership in Energy and Environmental Design for Existing Buildings (LEED-EB) rating system, which maximizes building operational efficiency while minimizing environmental impacts. It is a recognized, performance-based benchmark for building owners and operators to measure operations, improvements, and maintenance on a consistent scale. LEED-EB is designed for delivering economically profitable, environmentally responsible, healthy, productive places to live and work and provides a roadmap to building owners and managers on green cleaning. Contact it at U.S. Green Building Council, 1800 Massachusetts Ave., NW, Suite 300, Washington, DC, 20036. Phone: 202-828-7422.

Appendix B

Resources

●●

Programs/Associations

Center for a New Dream's Institutional Purchasing Program

This program and Web site tracks green purchasing programs from federal, state, and local governments and lists certified products, policies, and other information on green cleaning as well as other product categories such as paper, paint, and pest management. More information can be found at www.newdream.org/clean.

Commission for Environmental Cooperation (CEC)

The CEC is an international organization created by Canada, Mexico, and the United States to address regional environmental concerns, help prevent potential trade and environmental conflicts, and to promote the effective enforcement of environmental law. The CEC offers fact sheets on green cleaning and Web-based programs to help measure environmental impacts. Information can be found at www.cec.org.

EPA's Energy Star Program

This voluntary program provides an innovative energy performance rating system on a number of products and their partnership program for energy-efficient buildings is an essential part of the U.S. Green Building Council's LEED Rating Systems. Information can be found at www.energystar.gov.

EPA's Environmentally Preferable Purchasing Program

This voluntary program encourages and assists federal agencies in the purchasing of environmentally preferable products and services. The Web site includes federal guidance, tools, and other documents including those on green cleaning. More information can be found at www.epa.gov/epp.

EPA's Indoor Air Quality Tools for Schools

This voluntary program is designed to help schools with indoor air-quality issues. More information can be found at www.epa.gov/iaq/schools.

Green Cleaning Network

The Green Cleaning Network is a nonprofit whose mission is to use the marketplace to accelerate the adoption of green cleaning by facilitating the exchange of information, best practices, policies, model contract language, and so on. More information can be found at www.GreenCleaningNetwork.com. Steve is the founder and executive director of this entity.

Green Cleaning University (GCU)

An online e-learning program specifically focused on green cleaning. Classes include selecting green products, sales, program implementation, and more. GCU also sponsors special events such as programs with the U.S. Green Building Council, Green Seal, and the Commission on Environmental Cooperation. GCU can be found at www.GreenCleaningUniversity.org. This is co-owned by the authors.

Green Hotels Association

The Green Hotels Association has hundreds of hotel members all across the U.S. and helps them implement greener practices including cleaning, linen services, water conservation, and more. They also offer a catalog of approved products. More information can be found at www.greenhotels.com.

Green Restaurant Association

The Green Restaurant Association (GRA) provides services in research, consulting, education, marketing, and community organizing. The GRA utilizes a collaborative strategy that involves restaurants, manufacturers, vendors, grassroots organizations, government, media, and restaurant customers. More information can be found at www.dinegreen.com.

Hospitals for a Healthy Environment (H2E)

With more than 6,400 health care facilities including 1,500 hospitals, H2E promotes green initiatives including green cleaning and waste management in health care. Cleaning organizations can join and support H2E in a number of ways. More information can be found at www.h2e-online.org.

Healthy Schools Campaign

This nonprofit organization advocates for policies and model programs that allow students and staff members to learn and work in a healthy school environment. Cleaning organizations can help implement its Quick & Easy Guide to Green Cleaning in Schools, which is supported by the major school organizations. More information can be found at www.HealthySchoolsCampaign.org.

Publications

Collaborative for High Performance Schools (CHPS) Volume IV

Volume IV of the CHPS program provides specific guidelines for operations and maintenance of green schools, and contains a specific chapter (authored by Steve) that provides detailed recommendations for green cleaning. More information can be found at www.chps.net/manual.

DestinationGreen

The authors' free monthly e-newsletter specifically designed to help the cleaning industry implement green cleaning programs.

Each issue of *DestinationGreen* provides articles on green selling tips, interviews with experts, green in the news, and more. *DestinationGreen* can be found at www.DestinationGreen.com.

Environmental Building News

Environmental Building News (EBN) is a monthly newsletter featuring comprehensive, practical information on a wide range of topics related to sustainable building from energy efficiency and recycled-content materials to land-use planning and indoor air quality. Information on EBN can be found at www.buildinggreen.com/ecommerce/ebn.cfm.

Guidelines for Creating High-Performance Buildings

This publication was developed by the Commonwealth of Pennsylvania and provides information on green cleaning, land-scaping, lighting, HVAC maintenance, and more. To find it online, go to www.dgs.state.pa.us/ and search for "greenbuildingbook".

ManagingGreen

A free monthly e-newsletter specifically designed to help facility managers implement green programs. Each issue of *ManagingGreen* provides articles on a variety of green issues such as energy management, green purchasing, interviews with experts, green cleaning, green in the news, and more. *ManagingGreen* can be found at www.ManagingGreen.com. This newsletter is co-sponsored by The Ashkin Group, co-author Steve's company.

Office of the Federal Environmental Executive (OFEE)

This White House office is responsible for all of the federal environmental initiatives including those on green cleaning and is the repository for environmental executive orders, case studies, government initiatives, and more. Find in online at www.ofee.gov.

Quick & Easy Guide to Green Cleaning in Schools

This program was developed by the Healthy Schools Campaign along with the major school organizations, written by co-author Steve. The guide includes more than 300 pages of information on a variety of topics all related to green cleaning in schools. You can order the guide at www.healthyschoolscampaign.org/campaign/green_clean_schools/partnership.php.

Safe and Healthy School Environments

This is an excellent reference book edited by Howard Frumpkin and contains chapters on a number of important health, performance, building, and environmental issues specific to schools. The book is available from Oxford University Press. Steve co-authored the chapter on cleaning.

Ten Steps to Implementing Green Cleaning in Healthcare

This program guide was developed by Hospitals for a Healthy Environment (H2E) and lays out the steps to implementing green cleaning in a health-care setting. The document can be found at www.h2e-online.org. Steve is a contributor to this.

Index